OXFORD WO~~RLD~~

THE MAR

AND OTHE

DAVID BRADSHAW is Hawtl
Literature at Worcester Col   .. ⌐ı the
English Association. Editor o⌐   .. *Huxley* and *Brave New
World* (both 1994), Oxford World's Classics editions of *The White
Peacock* (1997), *Women in Love* (1998), and *Mrs Dalloway* (2000),
and Penguin editions of *Decline and Fall* and *The Good Soldier* (both
2001), he has published articles on Bloomsbury, Conrad, T. S. Eliot,
Huxley, Woolf, Yeats, and various aspects of literature and thought
in the 1930s. He is Victorian and Modern Literature Editor of the
Review of English Studies.

OXFORD WORLD'S CLASSICS

*For over 100 years Oxford World's Classics have brought
readers closer to the world's great literature. Now with over 700
titles—from the 4,000-year-old myths of Mesopotamia to the
twentieth century's greatest novels—the series makes available
lesser-known as well as celebrated writing.*

*The pocket-sized hardbacks of the early years contained
introductions by Virginia Woolf, T. S. Eliot, Graham Greene,
and other literary figures which enriched the experience of reading.
Today the series is recognized for its fine scholarship and
reliability in texts that span world literature, drama and poetry,
religion, philosophy and politics. Each edition includes perceptive
commentary and essential background information to meet the
changing needs of readers.*

OXFORD WORLD'S CLASSICS

VIRGINIA WOOLF

The Mark on the Wall
and Other Short Fiction

Edited with an Introduction and Notes by
DAVID BRADSHAW

OXFORD
UNIVERSITY PRESS

OXFORD
UNIVERSITY PRESS

Great Clarendon Street, Oxford OX2 6DP

Oxford University Press is a department of the University of Oxford.
It furthers the University's objective of excellence in research, scholarship,
and education by publishing worldwide in

Oxford New York

Athens Auckland Bangkok Bogotá Buenos Aires Cape Town
Chennai Dar es Salaam Delhi Florence Hong Kong Istanbul Karachi
Kolkata Kuala Lumpur Madrid Melbourne Mexico City Mumbai Nairobi
Paris São Paulo Shanghai Singapore Taipei Tokyo Toronto Warsaw

with associated companies in Berlin Ibadan

Oxford is a registered trade mark of Oxford University Press
in the UK and in certain other countries

British Library Cataloguing in Publication Data

Data available

Library of Congress Cataloging in Publication Data

Data available

ISBN 978–0–19–955499–7
4

Typeset in Ehrhardt
by RefineCatch Limited, Bungay, Suffolk
Printed in Great Britain by
Clays Ltd, St Ives plc

CONTENTS

BIOGRAPHICAL PREFACE

VIRGINIA WOOLF was born Adeline Virginia Stephen on 25 January 1882 at 22 Hyde Park Gate, Kensington. Her father, Leslie Stephen, himself a widower, had married in 1878 Julia Jackson, widow of Herbert Duckworth. Between them they already had four children; a fifth, Vanessa, was born in 1879, a sixth, Thoby, in 1880. There followed Virginia and, in 1883, Adrian.

Both of the parents had strong family associations with literature. Leslie Stephen was the son of Sir James Stephen, a noted historian, and brother of Sir James Fitzjames Stephen, a distinguished lawyer and writer on law. His first wife was a daughter of Thackeray, his second had been an admired associate of the Pre-Raphaelites, and also, like her first husband, had aristocratic connections. Stephen himself is best remembered as the founding editor of the *Dictionary of National Biography*, and as an alpinist, but he was also a remarkable journalist, biographer, and historian of ideas; his *History of English Thought in the Eighteenth Century* (1876) is still of great value. No doubt our strongest idea of him derives from the character of Mr Ramsay in *To the Lighthouse*; for a less impressionistic portrait, which conveys a strong sense of his centrality in the intellectual life of the time, one can consult Noël Annan's *Leslie Stephen* (revised edition, 1984).

Virginia had the free run of her father's library, a better substitute for the public school and university education she was denied than most women of the time could aspire to; her brothers, of course, were sent to Clifton and Westminster. Her mother died in 1895, and in that year she had her first breakdown, possibly related in some way to the sexual molestation of which her half-brother George Duckworth is accused. By 1897 she was able to read again, and did so voraciously: 'Gracious, child, how you gobble', remarked her father, who, with a liberality and good sense at odds with the age in which they lived, allowed her to choose her reading freely. In other respects her relationship with her father was difficult; his deafness and melancholy, his excessive emotional-ism, not helped by successive bereavements, all increased her nervousness.

Stephen fell ill in 1902 and died in 1904. Virginia suffered another breakdown, during which she heard the birds singing in Greek, a language in which she had acquired some competence. On her recovery she moved, with her brothers and sister, to a house in Gordon Square, Bloomsbury; there, and subsequently at several other nearby addresses, what eventually became famous as the Bloomsbury Group took shape.

Virginia had long considered herself a writer. It was in 1905 that she began to write for publication in the *Times Literary Supplement*. In her circle (more loosely drawn than is sometimes supposed) were many whose names are now half-forgotten, but some were or became famous: J. M. Keynes and E. M. Forster and Roger Fry; also Clive Bell, who married Vanessa, Lytton Strachey, who once proposed marriage to her, and Leonard Woolf. Despite much ill health in these years, she travelled a good deal, and had an interesting social life in London. She did a little adult-education teaching, worked for female suffrage, and shared the excitement of Roger Fry's Post-Impressionist Exhibition in 1910. In 1912, after another bout of nervous illness, she married Leonard Woolf.

She was thirty, and had not yet published a book, though *The Voyage Out* was in preparation. It was accepted for publication by her half-brother Gerald Duckworth in 1913 (it appeared in 1915). She was often ill with depression and anorexia, and in 1913 attempted suicide. But after a bout of violent madness her health seemed to settle down, and in 1917 a printing press was installed at Hogarth House, Richmond, where she and her husband were living. The Hogarth Press, later an illustrious institution, but at first meant in part as therapy for Virginia, was now inaugurated. She began *Night and Day*, and finished it in 1918. It was pub-lished by Duckworth in 1919, the year in which the Woolfs bought Monk's House, Rodmell, for £700. There, in 1920, she began *Jacob's Room*, finished, and published by the Woolfs' own Hogarth Press, in 1922. In the following year she began *Mrs*

Dalloway (finished in 1924, published 1925), when she was already working on *To the Lighthouse* (finished and published, after intervals of illness, in 1927). *Orlando*, a fantastic 'biography' of a man–woman, and a tribute to Virginia's close friendship with Vita Sackville-West, was written quite rapidly over the winter of 1927–8, and published, with considerable success, in October. *The Waves* was written and rewritten in 1930 and 1931 (published in October of that year). She had already started on *Flush*, the story of Elizabeth Barrett Browning's pet dog—another success with the public—and in 1932 began work on what became *The Years*.

This brief account of her work during the first twenty years of her marriage is of course incomplete; she had also written and published many shorter works, as well as both series of *The Common Reader*, and *A Room of One's Own*. There have been accounts of the marriage very hostile to Leonard Woolf, but he can hardly be accused of cramping her talent or hindering the development of her career.

The Years proved an agonizingly difficult book to finish, and was completely rewritten at least twice. Her friend Roger Fry having died in 1934, she planned to write a biography, but illnesses in 1936 delayed the project; towards the end of that year she began instead the polemical *Three Guineas*, published in 1938. *The Years* had meanwhile appeared in 1937, by which time she was again at work on the Fry biography, and already sketching in her head the book that was to be *Between the Acts*. *Roger Fry* was published in the terrifying summer of 1940. By the autumn of that year many of the familiar Bloomsbury houses had been destroyed or badly damaged by bombs. Back at Monk's House, she worked on *Between the Acts*, and finished it in February 1941. Thereafter her mental condition deteriorated alarmingly, and on 28 March, unable to face another bout of insanity, she drowned herself in the River Ouse.

Her career as a writer of fiction covers the years 1912–41, thirty years distracted by intermittent serious illness as well as by the demands, which she regarded as very important, of family and friends, and by the need or desire to write literary criticism and social comment. Her industry was extraordinary—nine highly-wrought novels, two or three of them among the great masterpieces of the form in this century, along with all the other writings, including the copious journals and letters that have been edited and published in recent years. Firmly set though her life was in the 'Bloomsbury' context—the agnostic ethic transformed from that of her forebears, the influence of G. E. Moore and the Cambridge Apostles, the individual brilliance of J. M. Keynes, Strachey, Forster, and the others—we have come more and more to value the distinctiveness of her talent, so that she seems more and more to stand free of any context that might be thought to limit her. None of that company—except, perhaps, T. S. Eliot, who was on the fringe of it—did more to establish the possibilities of literary innovation, or to demonstrate that such innovation must be brought about by minds familiar with the innovations of the past. This is true originality. It was Eliot who said of *Jacob's Room* that in that book she had freed herself from any compromise between the traditional novel and her original gift; it was the freedom he himself sought in *The Waste Land*, published in the same year, a freedom that was dependent upon one's knowing with intimacy that with which compromise must be avoided, so that the knowledge became part of the originality. In fact she had 'gobbled' her father's books to a higher purpose than he could have understood.

Frank Kermode

INTRODUCTION

The Proper Stuff for Fiction

Two of the stories in this collection, 'The Mark on the Wall' and 'An Unwritten Novel', begin with a reader's attention being grabbed by something other than writing; a third, 'In the Orchard', commences with a former reader fast asleep, her book having 'fallen into the grass' (p. 60) beside her chair, while soon after the start of a fourth, 'A Haunted House', the narrator speaks of 'stopping the pencil on the margin. And then, tired of reading' going off in pursuit of 'a ghostly couple'. A few lines further on another book has 'slipped into the grass' (p. 30). 'Such an expression of unhappiness was enough by itself,' the narrator of 'An Unwritten Novel' explains, 'to make one's eyes slide above the paper's edge to the poor woman's face—insignificant without that look, almost a symbol of human destiny with it' (p. 18), but the narrator of 'The Mark on the Wall' is distracted by nothing more than 'a small round mark, black upon a white wall' (p. 3). However, what might seem an unpropitious motif—readers finding sleep, day-dreams, or their surroundings more appealing than printed words—could not more neatly pinpoint Woolf's emphasis in these stories. Just as her fictional readers are captivated by things which lack identity, definition, or apparent significance, so readers of Woolf's short stories are drawn into the more fugitive recesses of the everyday, offered new angles on the ordinary, and brought face to face with the marginal and the marginalized, the obscure and the overlooked. The first eight pieces in this volume, in particular, explore aspects of human experience which would have been regarded by both earlier exponents of the short story and Woolf's more traditionalist peers as simply too insubstantial, uninteresting, or ephemeral to be worth writing about. Woolf proved otherwise.

These first eight stories ('The Mark on the Wall' through to 'A Society') comprised the only collection of short fiction Woolf published in her lifetime, *Monday or Tuesday* (1921). She had written her first short stories in 1906, and had been experimenting with the possibilities of the form from early in 1917, not least as an escape from her labours with the increasingly prolix and wearisome *Night and Day*, her second novel, published in 1919. On 26 July 1917, with 'The Mark on the Wall', her first published story, having just appeared in print, Woolf complained that she was finding the constraints of her novel in progress 'clumsy and overpowering . . . still if one could only get hold of them it would be superb. I daresay one ought to invent a completely new form. Anyhow its very amusing to try with these short things, and the greatest mercy to be able to do what one likes.'[1] Although *Night and Day* eventually grew to such a length that it seems designedly tedious, its juggernaut bulk and sheer uneventfulness seeming to lay bare the futility of fiction even attempting to reflect and bring shape to reality, Woolf's second novel also holds evidence of her burgeoning interest in the symbolic economy of the short story. Its heroine, Katharine Hilbery, for instance, prefers 'the exactitude, the star-like impersonality, of [mathematical] figures to the confusion, agitation, and vagueness of the finest prose',[2] and in almost the last paragraph of the novel Katharine looks at her companion, Ralph Denham, and attempts to follow 'the track of his thought':

She felt him trying to piece together in a laborious and elementary fashion fragments of belief, unsoldered and separate, lacking the unity of phrases fashioned by the old believers. Together they groped in this difficult region, where the unfinished, the unfulfilled, the unwritten, the unreturned, came together in their ghostly way and wore the semblance of the complete and the satisfactory. (p. 534)

This was precisely the 'difficult region' in which Woolf herself had been and was still 'grop[ing]' as she attempted to 'piece together' her own conception of the short story. Her labours were not misspent, as it was her efforts to capture the fragmentary, the absent, 'the unfinished, the unfulfilled, the unwritten' in her

[1] *The Letters of Virginia Woolf*, ed. Nigel Nicolson and Joanne Trautmann (6 vols.; London: Hogarth Press, 1975–80), ii. 167.

[2] *Night and Day*, ed. Suzanne Raitt, Oxford World's Classics (Oxford: OUP, 1992), 42.

short fiction which enabled Woolf to forge a clean break with the 'phrases fashioned by the old believers' in *Jacob's Room* (1922) and the other major novels that followed it. Had Woolf not experimented with short fiction in 1917–20, it seems certain that she would not have flourished so readily as a novelist in the early 1920s.

Six months before the appearance of *Night and Day* (on 20 October 1919) Woolf published a key essay in the *Times Literary Supplement* in which she set out both her opposition to the conventions of the mainstream novel and her own vision as a writer. In 'Modern Novels', Woolf identified 'a living, breathing, every-day imperfection' in three of the most celebrated novelists of her day: H. G. Wells (1866–1946), Arnold Bennett (1867–1931), and John Galsworthy (1867–1933). She characterizes this trio as 'materialists' and notes how the form and technique of their novels, and their approach to fiction in general, 'more and more ceases to resemble the vision in our minds. So much of the enormous labour of proving the solidity, the likeness to life, of the story is not merely labour thrown away but labour misplaced . . .'. A little further on, in a passage which is just as crucial to an understanding of what inspired her short fiction as it is to a study of her development as a novelist, Woolf continued:

Is it not possible that the accent falls a little differently, that the moment of importance came before or after, that, if one were free and could set down what one chose, there would be no plot, little probability, and a vague general confusion in which the clear-cut features of the tragic, the comic, the passionate, and the lyrical were dissolved beyond the possibility of separate recognition? The mind, exposed to the ordinary course of life, receives upon its surface a myriad impressions—trivial, fantastic, evanescent, or engraved with the sharpness of steel. From all sides they come, an incessant shower of innumerable atoms, composing in their sum what we might venture to call life itself; and to figure further as the semi-transparent envelope, or luminous halo, surrounding us from the beginning of consciousness to the end. Is it not perhaps the chief task of the novelist to convey this incessantly varying spirit with whatever stress or sudden deviation it may display, and as little admixture of the alien and external as possible? We are not pleading merely for courage and sincerity; but suggesting that the proper stuff for fiction is a little other than custom would have us believe it . . . Let us record the atoms as they fall upon the mind in the order in which they fall, let us trace the pattern, however disconnected and incoherent in appearance, which each sight or incident scores upon the consciousness. Let us not take it for granted that life exists more in what is commonly thought big than in what is commonly thought small'.[3]

These statements amount to nothing less than a manifesto, and Woolf kept up her attack on Wells, Bennett, and Galsworthy's projection of 'a vast sense of things in general; but a very vague one of things in particular' in later essays such as 'Mr Bennett and Mrs Brown' (1923)—from where this last quotation is borrowed—'Character in Fiction' (1924), and 'Modern Fiction' (1925). 'The capture of Mrs Brown', Woolf predicted in the first of these three essays (i.e. the attempt to represent in fiction the quirky, hazy, discontinuous imponderability of real life and individual psychology), 'is the title of the next chapter in the history of literature; and let us prophesy again, that chapter will be one of the most important, the most illustrious, the most epoch-making of them all.'[4]

An Intoxicating Sense of Freedom

Conveying the mind's bombardment by a 'myriad impressions' is the 'chief task' of a number of these stories. Continuously in 'The Mark on the Wall', for instance, the narrator's 'thoughts swarm upon a new object, lifting it a little way, as ants carry a blade of straw so feverishly, and then leave it' (p. 3). Though daunted by 'the mystery of life!' and her sense of 'what an accidental affair this living is after all our civilization' (p. 4), the narrator feels

---

[3] 'Modern Novels', repr. in *The Essays of Virginia Woolf*, ed. Andrew McNeillie (6 vols.: London: Hogarth Press, 1986–), iii. 30–7. First published in the *TLS* on 10 April 1919, this essay reappeared in a substantially revised form as 'Modern Fiction' in 1925 (repr. in *Essays*, iv. 157–65).

[4] *Essays*, iii. 384–9. 'Character in Fiction' is repr. on pp. 420–38. For 'Modern Fiction', see *Essays*, iv. 157–65.

more powerfully a sense of emancipation, and is happy 'to slip easily from one thing to another, without any sense of hostility, or obstacle ... to sink deeper and deeper, away from the surface, with its hard separate facts' (p. 5). By the end of the story, when the narrator asks 'Where was I? What has it all been about? A tree? A river? The Downs? Whitaker's Almanack? The fields of asphodel?', some readers may well be asking similar questions. But to ask them too insistently would be to have missed the point. As early as August 1908 Woolf told a correspondent that she was thinking 'a great deal of my future ... how I shall ... capture multitudes of things at present fugitive, enclose the whole, and shape infinite strange shapes',[5] and she achieves this first in her short fiction of 1917–20. Significantly, the opening sentence of both 'The Mark on the Wall' and 'Kew Gardens' contains the word 'perhaps', as if signing from the outset the caprice and provisionality of these fictions and accentuating their concern with the essential mystery of life: 'nothing is known' (p. 8). The narrator of 'The Mark on the Wall' rejoices in the fact that

there is not one reflection but an almost infinite number; those are the depths [novelists in future] will explore, those the phantoms they will pursue, leaving the description of reality more and more out of their stories, taking a knowledge of it for granted ... (p. 6)

Other stories reinforce this notion of the real as manifold and unfathomable. 'In the Orchard', for example, which presents the same scene in three different ways in the space of three pages, destabilizes any idea that art reflects in a straightforward way a single reality and suggests instead that the real is as arbitrary as it is 'shifting'.

'The Mark on the Wall' is brought to an abrupt end when the narrator senses someone 'standing over [her]' (p. 10). It is almost certainly a man, and, after announcing that he is 'going out to buy a newspaper' (p. 10), he reveals the mark on the wall to be nothing more than a snail. An experience which for the narrator has been cryptic, enthralling, and uplifting is terminated with the suddenness of a pistol shot. The non-narrative voice, brusque and

[5] *Letters*, i. 356.

denotative, acts as nothing more than an obstruction, checking the flow of the narrator's stream of consciousness. Yet what remains in the reader's mind is the connotative suppleness of the narrator's engagement with her world, the possibility she envisages of an alternative to

the masculine point of view which governs our lives, which sets the standard, which establishes Whitaker's Table of Precedency, which has become . . . since the war half a phantom to many men and women, which soon, one may hope, will be laughed into the dustbin where the phantoms go . . . leaving us all with an intoxicating sense of illegitimate freedom . . . (p. 7)

A sense of radical liberation, a refusal to be held fast by convention, is everywhere apparent in this short fiction, and two stories which are particularly charged with 'an intoxicating sense of illegitimate freedom' are 'Solid Objects' and 'A Society'. Although at the beginning of 'Solid Objects', when the mustachioed John and Charles are first sighted on the beach in their 'tweed caps, rough boots, shooting coats, [and] check stockings' arguing with pipes ablaze, 'nothing was so solid, so living, so hard, red, hirsute and virile as these two bodies for miles and miles of sea and sandhill' (p. 54), John's world is poised to lose its solidity when he burrows his fingers into the sand and discovers a 'large irregular lump' (p. 55) of glass. He takes it home and places it on his mantelpiece, where it soon (in yet another example of the distracted reader motif noted at the beginning of this Introduction) becomes 'a natural stopping place for the young man's eyes when they wandered from his book' (p. 56). In view of Woolf's antagonism to the 'materialists' it is nicely ironic that 'so hard, so concentrated, so definite an object' (p. 55) is responsible for John's almost immediate descent into a world of obsessive association:

John found himself attracted to the windows of curiosity shops when he was out walking, merely because he saw something which reminded him of the lump of glass. Anything . . . even the smooth oval egg of a prehistoric bird would do. He took, also, to keeping his eyes upon the ground, especially in the neighbourhood of waste land where the household refuse is thrown away. (p. 56)

John's enthusiasm for discarded things soon includes shards and he also begins 'to haunt the places which are most prolific of broken china, such as pieces of waste land between railway lines, sites of demolished houses, and commons in the neighbourhood of London' (pp. 57–8). His next find is a 'meteorite' and it is not long before his career as a barrister has been neglected and his parliamentary aspirations forgotten. John's 'intoxicating sense of illegitimate freedom' rapidly turns into a mania as he finally leaves hold of the patriarchal, common-sensical world of reason and sobriety for good:

Provided with a bag and a long stick fitted with an adaptable hook, [John] ransacked all deposits of earth; raked beneath matted tangles of scrub; searched all alleys and spaces between walls where he had learned to expect to find objects . . . thrown away. As his standard became higher and his taste more severe the disappointments were innumerable, but always some gleam of hope, some piece of china or glass curiously marked or broken, lured him on. (p. 59)

John's probings are the absurd counterpart of Woolf's own attraction to areas of human experience which many writers would have regarded as an unpromising 'waste land', strictly off limits.

'A Society' was written as a riposte to Arnold Bennett's *Our Women: Chapters on the Sex-Discord* (1920), in which he argued 'that intellectually and creatively man is the superior of woman, and that in the region of creative intellect there are things which men almost habitually do but which women have not done and give no sign of ever being able to do'.[6] On 26 September 1920 Woolf wrote in her diary that she was 'making up a paper upon Women, as a counterblast to Mr Bennett's adverse views reported in the papers'[7] and this turned into 'A Society'. Focused on a society formed by women to enquire into the world of men, this story is probably the most satirical single work Woolf produced

[6] Arnold Bennett, *Our Women: Chapters on the Sex-Discord* (London, New York, Toronto, and Melbourne: Cassell, 1920), 101.

[7] *The Diary of Virginia Woolf*, ed. Anne Olivier Bell and Andrew McNeillie (5 vols.; London: Hogarth Press, 1977–84), ii. 69.

and it is a worthy forerunner of *A Room of One's Own* (1929) and
Three Guineas (1938). Few of the 'things which men almost
habitually do' escape Woolf's scorn and the opening lines of the
story capture 'A Society''s pugnaciously tongue-in-cheek tone:

This is how it all came about. Six or seven of us were sitting one day
after tea. Some were gazing across the street into the windows of a
milliner's shop where the light still shone brightly upon scarlet feathers and golden slippers. Others were idly occupied in building little
towers of sugar upon the edge of the tea tray. After a time . . . we drew
round the fire and began as usual to praise men—how strong, how
noble, how brilliant, how courageous, how beautiful they were—how
we envied those who by hook or by crook managed to get attached to
one for life . . . (p. 40)

From this point on, prominent institutions of the masculine
world, such as the Royal Navy, the legal profession, the Royal
Academy, and Oxbridge, are sniped at with relish and, not sur-
prisingly, Bennett himself takes some flak. One of the women,
when asked whether Bennett, Wells, and others 'write good
books', looks at the ceiling before responding:

'You must remember,' she began, speaking with extreme rapidity, 'that
fiction is the mirror of life. And you can't deny that education is of the
highest importance, and that it would be extremely annoying, if you
found yourself alone at Brighton late at night, not to know which was
the best boarding house to stay at . . .'
    'But what has that got to do with it?' we asked.
    'Nothing—nothing—nothing whatever' she replied. (p. 50)

Here Woolf is attacking (as she had done in 'Modern Novels' the
year before) the materialists' concern with social ambience and
incidental detail rather than interior truth. After a gap of five
years the narrator finds herself with Castalia, 'in the room where
our meetings used to be held', and the jabbing at Bennett
resumes. Castalia says that she has tried

to prevent my little girl from learning to read, but what's the use? I
caught Ann only yesterday with a newspaper in her hand and she was
beginning to ask me if it was 'true'. Next she'll ask me . . . whether Mr
Arnold Bennett is a good novelist, and finally whether I believe in

God. How can I bring my daughter up to believe in nothing?' she demanded. (p. 52)

Only in the fantastic realm of 'Lappin and Lapinova' is there some kind of temporary concord between the sexes, and even there it is based on nothing more than a grotesque and unequal complementarity:

They were the very opposite of each other; he was bold and deter-mined; she wary and undependable. He ruled over the busy world of rabbits; her world was a desolate, mysterious place, which she ranged mostly by moonlight. All the same, their territories touched; they were King and Queen of the land of rabbits and hares. (p. 86)

An Emphasis on Unexpected Places

Alongside the other issues which she addresses in 'Character in Fiction', Woolf asks herself 'what is reality?' This question, and the problem of whether reality could be mirrored in art, had become increasingly contentious during the course of the nine-teenth century.[8] In the twentieth century, however, modernists such as Woolf and James Joyce recognized that the upheavals of Einstein and Freud, among others, compelled the artist to acknowledge that only partial truths were available, not the whole truth, and that fiction must always and inevitably reflect but an aspect of reality if it reflected anything at all: narratorial omnisci-ence was merely an outmoded fallacy. This conviction shapes 'An Unwritten Novel'. Facing another woman in her railway carriage, the narrator conjures up her fellow traveller's destination, her social background, her past, her blighted hopes in love, the 'meagre[ness]' of her domestic surroundings, her loneliness, her God, and even her name: 'Minnie Marsh'. The narrator is con-vinced she has read the other woman accurately and that her narrative has gathered 'richness and rotundity, destiny and tra-gedy, as stories should' (p. 24). But the narrator, it seems, has got it all wrong. Her speculations are exposed as distortions when

---

[8] See e.g. Lilian R. Furst, *All is True: The Claims and Strategies of Realist Fiction* (Durham, NC and London: Duke University Press, 1995), 4–5.

'Minnie' is met at the station by her son and goes off with him 'side by side' and in high spirits. The narrator is momentarily 'confounded':

And yet the last look of them . . . floods me anew. Mysterious figures! Mother and son. Who are you? Why do you walk down the street? Where tonight will you sleep, and then, tomorrow? Oh, how it whirls and it surges—floats me afresh! I start after them . . . If I fall on my knees, if I go through the ritual, the ancient antics, it's you, unknown figures, you I adore, if I open my arms, it's you I embrace, you I draw to me—adorable world! (pp. 28–9)

The narrator's joyous acknowledgement that life is ultimately unpredictable and never quite what it seems was shared by Woolf herself.

On 26 January 1920 Woolf noted in her diary that she had that 'afternoon arrived at some idea of a new form for a new novel':

Suppose one thing should open out of another—as in An Unwritten Novel—not for 10 pages but 200 or so—doesn't that give the looseness & lightness I want: doesnt that get closer & yet keep form & speed, & enclose everything, everything? . . . [T]he approach will be entirely different this time: no scaffolding; scarcely a brick to be seen; all crepuscular, but the heart, the passion, humour, everything as bright as fire in the mist . . . Whether I'm sufficiently mistress of things—that's the doubt; but conceive the mark on the wall, K[ew]. G[ardens]. & unwritten novel taking hands and dancing in unity.[9]

The publication of *Jacob's Room* two years later proved that her 'doubt' had been unfounded, that her experiments with short fiction had paid off, and that she was now, indeed, 'mistress of things'. Looking back in 1930, she told her friend Ethel Smyth that the stories which became *Monday or Tuesday* 'were written by way of diversion' when her health was poor and the struggle with *Night and Day* seemed unending:

they were the treats I allowed myself when I had done my exercise in the conventional style. I shall never forget the day I wrote The Mark on the Wall—all in a flash, as if flying, after being kept stone breaking for months. The Unwritten Novel was the great discovery, however.

[9] *Diary*, ii. 13–14.

That—again in one second—showed me how I could embody all my deposit of experience in a shape that fitted it—not that I have ever reached that end; but anyhow I saw, branching out of the tunnel I made, when I discovered that method of approach, Jacob's Room, Mrs Dalloway etc—How I trembled with excitement; and then Leonard [her husband] came in, and I drank my milk, and concealed my excitement, and wrote I suppose another page of that interminable Night and Day.[10]

Woolf went on to remark: 'Green and Blue [*sic*] and the heron were the wild outbursts of freedom, inarticulate, ridiculous, unprintable mere outcries', and in comparison with the rounded and substantial short stories of Edgar Allan Poe, Robert Louis Stevenson, Rudyard Kipling, Henry James, and Somerset Maugham, Woolf's 'Blue and Green' and 'Monday or Tuesday', fictions pared to a minimum, might seem to be nothing more than 'mere outcries'. But as critics such as Clare Hanson have observed, 'one of [the] leading characteristics [of the modernist short story] is a rejection of "story" in the accepted sense.' Modernists such as Joyce, Katherine Mansfield, Gertrude Stein, and Woolf repudiated the polished coherence and narrative detachment of the traditional short story as a falsification of the modern condition. Instead, they placed their stress 'on a single moment of intense or significant experience'.[11] 'Monday or Tuesday', for example, is manifestly 'unfinished', 'unfulfilled', and 'unwritten' (to borrow, again, those three key terms from the *Night and Day* quotation near the beginning of the Introduction); its lack of scene-setting and its swooping, darting impressionism create a work which is both extempore and melodic, less a story than a 'leaf-light' (p. 32) collage of nuance. As a contemporary reviewer observed, ' "Monday or Tuesday" is an example of the "unrepresentational" art which is creeping across from painting to see what it can make of words. It sounds beautiful; it suggests beautiful, or at least life-full things—the heron flying, the busy street, the

---

[10] *Letters*, iv. 231.

[11] Clare Hanson, *Short Stories and Short Fictions, 1880–1980* (London and Basingstoke: Macmillan, 1985), 55.

fire-lit room . . .'.[12] T. S. Eliot, another admirer of Woolf's short
fiction, put it differently but made a similar claim for her work:

A good deal of the secret of the charm of Mrs Woolf's shorter pieces
consists in the immense disparity between the object and the train of
feeling which it has set in motion. Mrs Woolf gives you the minutest
datum, and leads you to explore, quite consciously, the sequence of
images and feelings which float away from it. The result is something
which makes Walter Pater appear an unsophisticated rationalist, and
the writing is often remarkable.[13]

Although not as succinct as 'Monday or Tuesday' or 'Blue and
Green', the narrative voice of 'A Haunted House' is equally dif-
ficult to pin down, while 'Kew Gardens', 'The Mark on the Wall',
'The String Quartet', 'In the Orchard', and 'An Unwritten
Novel' all display in abundance the licence, fluidity, and
unexpectedness which Woolf found in Chekhov's short stories:

The emphasis is laid upon such unexpected places that at first it seems
as if there were no emphasis at all; and then, as the eyes accustom
themselves to twilight and discern the shapes of things in a room, we
see how complete the story is, how profound, and how truly in obedi-
ence to his vision Tchehov has chosen this, that, and the other, and
placed them together to compose something new.[14]

The Sound that Reverberates

In *The Voyage Out*, Woolf's first novel, published in 1915, a clear
link is established between masculinity, machinery, and the power
of the state.[15] Woolf shows how they combine in a way which
is deeply inimical to women in general and the individual in

---

[12] Unsigned rev. [by Harold Child], *TLS* (7 April 1921), 227. Repr. in Robin
Majumdar and Allen McLaurin (eds.), *Virginia Woolf: The Critical Heritage* (1975;
London: Routledge, 1997), 87.

[13] T. S. Eliot, 'London Letter', *The Dial*, 71, No. 2 (August 1921), 216–17. The
aesthete Walter Pater (1839–94) was widely regarded as a master of prose.

[14] 'Modern Novels,' 35.

[15] For a discussion of this aspect of the novel see my 'Vicious Circles: Hegel, Bosan-
quet and *The Voyage Out*', in Diane F. Gillespie and Leslie K. Hankins (eds.), *Virginia
Woolf and the Arts: Selected Papers from the Sixth Annual Conference on Virginia Woolf*
(New York: Pace University Press, 1997), 183–91.

particular, and this idea is touched on in a number of these short stories. Following a reference to the punctuality and unstoppability of trains in 'An Unwritten Novel', for instance, the narrator declares: 'That's the man's way; that's the sound that reverberates; that's St Paul's and the motor-omnibuses' (p. 26), and in 'Monday or Tuesday', the silence, tranquillity, and timelessness of the first paragraph is disrupted when 'Wheels strike divergently' in the second: 'Omnibuses conglomerate in conflict . . . the clock asseverates with twelve distinct strokes that it is midday . . .' (p. 32). Woolf's verbs suggest the oppressive, ineluctable, mechanical grind of metropolitan experience; soon afterwards 'a van discharges' before peace is 'recollect[ed] by the fireside'. This juxtaposition of clocks and machinery on the one hand, and silence and individuality on the other was to be developed more fully in *Mrs Dalloway*, in which clock time epitomizes the intrusive power of the state.[16] The 'motor omnibuses . . . turning their wheels and changing their gear; like a vast nest of Chinese boxes all of wrought steel turning ceaselessly one within another' and bringing to a close the silence and stillness of 'Kew Gardens', is another example of the way in which Woolf focuses in these stories on the disparity between an exterior, masculine world of action, fragmentation, and noise, and an interior feminine sphere of silence, contact, unity, and reflection. Even in 'A Haunted House' a contrast is established between the near-silent ghosts who move about the house, and whose presence the narrator feels powerfully, and 'the hum of the threshing machine sounding from the farm' (p. 30) nearby.

If the marginalization of women is the most obvious real-world issue these stories address, the impact of the First World War on British society comes not too far behind. The War is perhaps most interestingly refracted in 'Kew Gardens', set during a wartime July between 1915 and 1918. Among the men and women who pass by the oval flower-bed are a very strange couple indeed:

The younger of the two wore an expression of unnatural calm; he raised his eyes and fixed them very steadily in front of him while his

---

[16] See my 'Introduction' to *Mrs Dalloway*, Oxford World's Classics (Oxford: OUP, 2000), pp. xxxii–xxxiv, xxxix–xli.

companion spoke, and directly his companion had done speaking he looked on the ground again and sometimes opened his lips only after a long pause and sometimes did not open them at all. The elder man had a curiously uneven and shaky method of walking, jerking his hand forward and throwing up his head abruptly, rather in the manner of an impatient carriage horse tired of waiting outside a house; but in the man these gestures were irresolute and pointless. He talked almost incessantly . . . He was talking about spirits—the spirits of the dead, who, according to him, were even now telling him all sorts of odd things about their experiences in Heaven. (p. 13)

The elder man's further remark that 'with this war, the spirit matter is rolling between the hills like thunder' (p. 13) and his description of a contraption through which widows may contact the dead, indicate that (like Sir Arthur Conan Doyle (1859–1930), the creator of Sherlock Holmes) he is a spiritualist. But the elder man's bizarre gait and talking aloud are also reminiscent of a victim of shell-shock, such as Septimus Warren Smith in *Mrs Dalloway*, while the younger man's 'expression of unnatural calm' looks equally neurasthenic. The pair are, in effect, both a half-crazed old spiritualist and his embarrassed son and symbolic convalescents, war casualties of a kind Woolf would have seen not just in Kew Gardens but all over London. Characteristically, even though Woolf's stress in this story is mainly on the smallest of things—such as pebbles, petals, and snails—and the transitoriness of experience, she cannot turn her gaze entirely from the greatest tragedy of her time. When 'Kew Gardens' was first published, the *TLS* 's reviewer argued that it provided 'new proof of the complete unimportance in art of the *hyle*, the subject-matter . . . here is "Kew Gardens"—a work of art, made, "created", as we say, finished, four-square; a thing of original and therefore strange beauty, with its own "atmosphere", its own vital force'.[17] This is largely, but not entirely, true of 'Kew Gardens' and Woolf's short fiction as a whole; but only rarely, in a piece such as 'Blue and Green', for example, is her work entirely free of *hyle*. She always has one eye on the real world even when she is writing against it.

---

[17] Unsigned rev. [by Harold Child], *TLS* (29 May 1919), 293. Repr. in Majumdar and McLaurin (eds.), *Virginia Woolf: The Critical Heritage*, 66–7.

There are a number of references to the Peace of Versailles in these stories, the treaty which brought the War to a formal end. Immediately after announcing that he is 'going out to buy a newspaper', for instance, the man who puts a stop to the narrator's thoughts in 'The Mark on the Wall' adds: 'Though it's no good buying newspapers . . . Nothing ever happens. Curse this war! God damn this war!' (p. 10). The War is both declared (p. 51) and concluded in 'A Society'. The last section of the story is set in 1919 when 'The war was over and peace was in process of being signed' (p. 51). 'While we spoke,' the narrator mentions a little further on, 'men were crying hoarsely and wearily in the street, and listening, we heard that the Treaty of Peace had just been signed' (p. 53). From this comment, we know that 'A Society' concludes on 28 June 1919. The signing of the Peace of Versailles is also mentioned in the second paragraph of 'The String Quartet', while 'An Unwritten Novel' is set on the day following the ratification of the Treaty on 10 January 1920: '"Peace between Germany and the Allied Powers was yesterday officially ushered in at Paris . . ."' (p. 18). In the same way that the Treaty of Versailles, signed in the palace's famous hall of mirrors, brought to an end the most tragic and catastrophic episode in the history of Europe and 'empowered the world to begin its life anew',[18] so Woolf seems to have identified the Treaty, for all its flaws and vindictiveness, with the final overthrow of the old epoch of realism and the dawn of the new order of modernism, the 'empower[ment]' of a new kind of writing.

Appropriately, in this respect, 'The Lady in the Looking-Glass: A Reflection' is more concerned with what is not reflected, more attentive to what is sliced off by the frame than what is held by the mirror. In the nineteenth century the mirror (or looking-glass) had been 'strongly favored by the realists as a cipher for the relationship between world and word',[19] but Woolf's story is about the fundamental instability of that relationship and how a frame is more a symbol of confinement than interpretation. The narrator, looking at the mirror from the drawing-room, feels

---

[18] 'Peace with Germany', *The Times* (12 January 1920), 13.
[19] Furst, *All is True*, 8–9.

surrounded by 'such shy creatures, lights and shadows, curtains blowing, petals falling ... Nothing stayed the same for two seconds together.' In the hall, however, 'the looking-glass reflected the hall table, the sunflowers, the garden path so accurately and so fixedly that they seemed held there in their reality unescapably. It was a strange contrast—all changing here, all stillness there' (p. 63). The narrator spends little time on what is actually reflected in the looking-glass and rather more time on her own reflections about what her host, Isabella Tyson, absent in the garden, is thinking and doing. She makes Isabella sound quite interesting, caring, and sociable, but when she enters the hall at the end of the story and the looking-glass begins 'to pour over her a light that seemed to fix her; that seemed like some acid to bite off the unessential and superficial and to leave only the truth', the narrator realizes that 'Isabella was perfectly empty. She had no thoughts. She had no friends. She cared for nobody' (p. 68). Given this contrast, the reader is left to consider what is the 'unessential' and what is 'the truth'—not just about Isabella Tyson, but life in general. Might the mirror be lying?

Disturbing Material

In a review of 1919, Woolf argued that the American realist Theodore Dreiser (1871–1945) 'lacked all the necessary qualities for a writer of short stories—concentration, penetration, form . . .'.[20] Woolf's early stories are replete with these qualities but the work she produced in the 1930s ('The Shooting Party' through to 'The Legacy') may seem at first to miss them. 'The Shooting Party', for example, begins with Milly Masters getting into 'a third-class railway carriage' (p. 76) in the foggy Midlands of England almost as if in homage to Arnold Bennett. Dressed 'out of fashion, as women dressed, years ago, in pictures in fashion plates of sporting newspapers' (p. 69), Milly would not have looked out of place in one of Bennett's Potteries novels. In addition, the titles of three of the four final stories start with a definite article and they are

---

[20] *Essays*, iii. 87.

clearly 'about' something in a way that 'Blue and Green' is not. In his discussion of Woolf's short fiction Dominic Head draws on Eileen Baldeshwiler's distinction 'between the conventional, plot-based story ("epical") and the "lyrical"' story, often open-ended, which focuses upon 'internal changes, moods, and feelings',[21] and the 1930s work clearly falls into the former category. However, while Woolf's later stories are unquestionably 'epical' in mode, they are far from conventional in subject matter and they disclose all the 'necessary qualities for a writer of short stories'.

'The Shooting Party' is a macabre story about women getting their own back. The Rashleighs came to prominence around the time of Elizabeth I through violence and the abuse of power—'Up the Amazons. Freebooters. Voyagers ... Taking captives. Maidens' (p. 70)—and nothing has changed in the twentieth century. Milly Masters, the housekeeper, 'scarred on the jaw' (p. 69), has borne not only the son of Hugh Rashleigh but probably his wrath as well, just as old Miss Rashleigh will meet her death after she is struck 'on the cheek' by the leather knotted tawse of her brutal brother, the current Squire. This pervasive violence explains why the two old women sit by and chuckle with indifference as their ancestral home, crumbling, damp, and assailed by the wind, falls down around them, just as Milly laughs to herself in the still-room at the big house and smiles to herself in the train, having left it.

'The Shooting Party' is a distinctly peculiar tale. Linden Peach has pointed out how it 'shares with *Between the Acts* [Woolf's last novel, posthumously published in 1941] a fusion of the apocalyptic with a dark carnivalesque':

The shooting party—an uneasy juxtaposition of the joyous with killing—signifies a muted but nevertheless real indifference to suffering evident also in the way in which Antonia and her sister chuckle over memories of the shooter who accidentally shot himself through the heart [Hugh Rashleigh] and John who, thrown from his horse, was ridden over by the hunt.[22]

[21] Dominic Head, *The Modernist Short Story: A Study in Theory and Practice* (Cambridge: Cambridge University Press, 1992), 79.
[22] Linden Peach, *Virginia Woolf* (Basingstoke and London: Macmillan, 2000), 195–7.

It was John, presumably, who fell for 'Lily . . . A bad 'un . . . Riding with a scarlet tassel on her cane', who provoked him to gallop 'as if he had twenty devils in him' (p. 74), as Miss Antonia recalls, while it was Hugh Rashleigh, probably, who was involved not only with Milly, but also with 'Lucy at the Mill' and 'Ellen's daughter at the Goat and Sickle'. All of these women, in one way or another, have played their role in bringing down the house of Rashleigh, just as mermaids were thought to be responsible for shipwrecks, and this is why old Miss Rashleigh raises her glass and appears to toast 'the mermaid carved in plaster on the fire-place' (p. 74) not long before she is crushed beneath it. It is the allure of the mermaid (once a name for a prostitute), of women's sexuality, which has proved irresistible and fatal to the house of Rashleigh. The enfeebled Squire knows this, and it is why he curses so savagely and lashes out with his tawse when he enters the room in which his elderly sisters are lunching. Although Miss Antonia and Miss Rashleigh are likened to the pheasants that are being slaughtered on the moors outside the house—'their laces and their flounces seemed to quiver, as if their bodies were warm and languid underneath their feathers as they drank' (p. 73)—and they await their 'slouching', weak-voiced, pheasant-shooting brother with some trepidation, they also look forward to their own and their family's end with pleasure. Similarly, the expression on Milly's face in the railway carriage suggests her ultimate triumph and revenge: 'why should not the eyes there, gleaming, moving, be the ghost of a family, of an age, of a civilization dancing over the grave?' (p. 76).

While 'The Shooting Party', 'Lappin and Lapinova', and 'The Legacy' actually have 'concentration, penetration, [and] form' (Woolf's prerequisites for the short story) in abundance and share a concern with concealed passion, betrayal, and the rejection of patriarchal values, it is noticeable that none of these 1930s stories directly engages with the specific anxieties of that decade, as do *The Years* (1937), *Three Guineas* (1938), and *Between the Acts* (1941). In no story is this apparent disregard for the apprehensions of the moment more striking than in 'The Duchess and the Jeweller', in one sense the most challenging of all the pieces in this volume and the most controversial text in Woolf's canon.

Elsewhere, I have argued that *The Years*, among other things, is a philo-Semitic novel in which Woolf confronts and contests the anti-Semitism of both her own social circles and the British Union of Fascists while also highlighting the long history and peaceful integration of the Jews in England.[23] But if there is any truth at all in this claim, how can it be squared with Woolf's treatment of Oliver Bacon in 'The Duchess and the Jeweller'? Bacon—even the name seems a calculated, heavy-handed affront—is from Whitechapel, a district of East London then heavily populated with Jewish refugees from European persecution. His mother, to whose memory, in caricature Jewish fashion, he is closely attached, is said to have concluded her remarks to him as a boy, in equally stock Jewish fashion, with 'my son' (p. 77). More troublingly, Bacon's nose is described as 'long and flexible, like an elephant's trunk' (p. 78) and this is not the only animal simile Woolf deploys. In his desire for social advancement, Bacon is said to be like 'a giant hog in a pasture rich with truffles' (p. 78) and he walks 'as the camel at the zoo sways from side to side' (p. 78). Having amused himself with the thought of blowing up Mayfair, we read that Bacon throws 'his head back and made a sound like a horse neighing' (p. 80). As if this is not enough, he has 'long pointed nails' and is said to have begun 'life in a filthy little alley' (p. 77). The archetypal self-made man as well as the stereotype Jew, Bacon is haughty with his staff and has (as confirmed by his Roman emperor cufflinks) an inflated opinion of himself. To contemporary readers, to Woolf's admirers, this story comes as quite a shock.

Two of the most surprising aspects of 'The Duchess and the Jeweller' are that Woolf worked on the story at precisely the same time as she worked on *Three Guineas*, her passionate, indignant critique of social exclusion and prejudice, and that the story was not further altered after Woolf was advised to take out specific

[23] 'Hyams Place: *The Years*, the Jews and the British Union of Fascists', in Maroula Joannou (ed.), *Women Writers of the 1930s: Gender, Politics and History* (Edinburgh: Edinburgh University Press, 1999), 179–91.

references to 'a little Jew boy' and 'crowds of Jewesses' by her New York literary agent. First published in 1938, 'The Duchess and the Jeweller' may well have been conceived six years previously. 'The inclusion of "The Great Jeweller" among the list of "Caricatures" (along with "Country House Life" and "The Royal Navy") that VW made in February 1932', Susan Dick tells us, 'suggests that a first draft of the story may have been written at this time . . . The two undated typescript drafts with holograph revisions that have survived were probably made in August 1937, when VW prepared the story for publication.'[24] But even if it did begin life as a caricature, by the time the story was published the representation and persecution of Jews, especially in Germany, had become a far more public and problematic issue than it had been in 1932. If writing this story in the first place was a doubtful act, revising it and sending it to New York for publication in the late 1930s adds up, at the very least, to a most strange and disturbing lapse of judgement on Woolf's part.

It is true that the story's other main character, a Gentile, is hardly more appealing than the jeweller. The Duchess of Lambourne, 'very large, very fat, tightly girt in pink taffeta, and past her prime' (p. 80), is far from attractive either in appearance or her morality. When Bacon and the Duchess shake hands

the link was forged between them once more. They were friends, yet enemies; he was master, she was mistress; each cheated the other, each needed the other, each feared the other. (p. 81)

The Duchess has lied to Bacon in the past and he allows himself to be gulled by her again. It is only at the end of the story, when Bacon discovers that the pearls are fakes, and when his vulnerability, his pathetic love for one of the Duchess's daughters, and his marginalization in a society which both despises and needs him is laid bare so effectively, that the more disquieting aspects of the story are almost redeemed. Indeed, Hermione Lee has argued that in 'writing such things' as 'The Duchess and the Jeweller',

---

[24] Susan Dick (ed.), *The Complete Shorter Fiction of Virginia Woolf* (1985; London: Hogarth Press, rev. edn. 1989), 308.

'Woolf separates herself off from the habitual, half-conscious anti-Semitism of her circle. She spells out her complicity in bigotry and offensiveness by way of self-accusation and social critique . . . The Jew in the story is the victim, as well as the exploiter, of the gentile duchess's greed and scorn . . .'.[25] Given that there is nothing quite like it in the rest of Woolf's *œuvre*, this interpretation is persuasive, but 'The Duchess and the Jeweller' is likely to remain Woolf's single most controversial piece of work, largely inexcusable, perhaps, definitely untypical, but well-crafted in spite of its offensive subject matter.[26]

With the notable exception of 'The Duchess and the Jeweller', the stories in this volume display many of the same virtues as Woolf's finest novels, being highly organized but lyrical, provocative yet elusive, deft but substantial. The best need to be read a number of times to do them justice, and they should be viewed not as inferior sideshows, diverting the reader's attention from the main attraction of the novels, but successful works of art in their own right, crucial elements in Woolf's development as a writer. A few, 'The Mark on the Wall', 'An Unwritten Novel', 'Kew Gardens', 'The Shooting Party', and 'The Legacy', are among the most interesting and accomplished fictions she wrote.

[25] Hermione Lee, *Virginia Woolf* (London: Chatto & Windus, 1996), 680.

[26] For a compact overview of Woolf's attitude to Jews in general and her Jewish husband and his family in particular, see ibid. 313–15.

NOTE ON THE TEXT

THE first eight stories in this collection were first gathered together as *Monday or Tuesday* (London: Hogarth Press, 1921), abbreviated to *MT*, the only volume of short fiction which Woolf published in her lifetime. The texts reprinted here are taken from that volume.

'The Mark on the Wall' was first published in July 1917 in a volume entitled *Two Stories* (the other story, 'Three Jews', was by Leonard Woolf) before being reprinted in 1919 and then included, in a slightly revised form, in *MT*; 'Kew Gardens' was first published on 12 May 1919, reprinted the following month, and then reprinted again in *MT*; 'An Unwritten Novel' first appeared in the *London Mercury* (July 1920), 273–80, before being slightly revised and included in *MT*; 'A Haunted House' was first published in *MT*; 'Monday or Tuesday' was first published in *MT*; 'Blue and Green' was first published in *MT*; 'The String Quartet' was first published in *MT*; 'A Society' was first published in *MT*; 'Solid Objects' first appeared in the *Athenaeum*, no. 4721 (22 October 1920), 543–5, and this is the text reprinted; 'In the Orchard' was first published in the *Criterion* 1, No. 3 (April 1923), 243–5, and this is the text reprinted; 'The Lady in the Looking-Glass: A Reflection' was first published in *Harper's Magazine*, 160 (December 1929), 46–9 in the version reprinted here; 'The Shooting Party' was first published in *Harper's Bazaar* (March 1938), 72, 100, 102, and this is the version reprinted here; 'The Duchess and the Jeweller' was first published in *Harper's Bazaar* (April 1938), 40–1, 116, 118 in the version reprinted here; 'Lappin and Lapinova' was first published in *Harper's Bazaar* (April 1939), 36–7, 96, 98, and this is the version reprinted here; 'The Legacy' was first published in the posthumous *A Haunted House and Other Short Stories*, with a Foreword by Leonard Woolf (London: Hogarth Press, 1943 [i.e. 1944]), and this is the text reprinted here.

SELECT BIBLIOGRAPHY

Bibliography

Kirkpatrick, B.J., and Clarke, Stuart N., *A Bibliography of Virginia Woolf* (4th edn.; Oxford: Clarendon Press, 1997).

Biography

Bell, Quentin, *Virginia Woolf: A Biography* (1972–3; London: Pimlico, 1996).

Gordon, Lyndall, *Virginia Woolf: A Writer's Life* (Oxford: Oxford University Press, 1984).

Leaska, Mitchell A., *Granite and Rainbow: The Hidden Life of Virginia Woolf* (London: Picador, 1998).

Lee, Hermione, *Virginia Woolf* (London: Chatto & Windus, 1996).

Mepham, John, *Virginia Woolf: A Literary Life* (London and Basingstoke: Macmillan, 1991).

Poole, Roger, *The Unknown Virginia Woolf* (4th edn.; Cambridge: Cambridge University Press, 1995).

Woolf, Leonard, *An Autobiography* (2 vols.; Oxford: Oxford University Press, 1980).

Editions

The Complete Shorter Fiction of Virginia Woolf, ed. Susan Dick (1985; London: Hogarth Press, rev. edn. 1989).

The Diary of Virginia Woolf, ed. Anne Olivier Bell and Andrew McNeillie (5 vols.; London: Hogarth Press, 1977–84).

The Essays of Virginia Woolf, ed. Andrew McNeillie (6 vols.; London: Hogarth Press, 1986–).

Letters of Leonard Woolf, ed. Frederic Spotts (London: Weidenfeld & Nicolson, 1989).

The Letters of Virginia Woolf, ed. Nigel Nicolson and Joanne Trautmann (6 vols.; London: Hogarth Press, 1975–80).

A Passionate Apprentice: The Early Journals 1897–1909, ed. Mitchell A. Leaska (London: Hogarth Press, 1990).

General Criticism

Abel, Elizabeth, *Virginia Woolf and the Fictions of Psychoanalysis* (Chicago: University of Chicago Press, 1989).

Beer, Gillian, *Virginia Woolf: The Common Ground* (Edinburgh: Edinburgh University Press, 1996).

Bowlby, Rachel (ed.), *Virginia Woolf*, Longman Critical Readers series (London: Longman, 1992).

—— *Virginia Woolf: Feminist Destinations and Further Essays on Virginia Woolf* (Edinburgh: Edinburgh University Press, 1997).

Briggs, Julia, *Virginia Woolf: Introductions to the Major Works* (London: Virago Press, 1994).

Clements, Patricia, and Grundy, Isobel (eds.) *Virginia Woolf: New Critical Essays* (London: Vision Press, 1983).

Fleishman, Avrom, *Virginia Woolf: A Critical Reading* (Baltimore: Johns Hopkins University Press, 1975).

Gillespie, Diane Filby, *The Sisters' Arts: The Writing and Painting of Virginia Woolf and Vanessa Bell* (Syracuse, NY: Syracuse University Press, 1988).

Goldman, Jane, *The Feminist Aesthetics of Virginia Woolf: Modernism, Post–Impressionism and the Politics of the Visual* (Cambridge: Cambridge University Press, 1998).

Hussey, Mark, *The Singing of the Real World: The Philosophy of Virginia Woolf's Fiction* (Columbus, Ohio: Ohio State University Press, 1986).

—— *Virginia Woolf A to Z: A Comprehensive Reference for Students, Teachers and Common Readers to her Life, Work and Critical Reception* (New York: Facts on File Inc., 1995).

—— (ed.) *Virginia Woolf and War: Fiction, Reality, and Myth* (Syracuse, NY: Syracuse University Press, 1991).

Laurence, Patricia Ondek, *The Reading of Silence: Virginia Woolf in the English Tradition* (Stanford, Calif.: Stanford University Press, 1991).

Lee, Hermione, *The Novels of Virginia Woolf* (London: Methuen, 1977).

McLaurin, Allen, *Virginia Woolf: The Echoes Enslaved* (Cambridge: Cambridge University Press, 1973).

Majumdar, Robin, and McLaurin, Allen (eds.), *Virginia Woolf: The Critical Heritage* (1975; London: Routledge, 1997).

Marcus, Jane (ed.), *New Feminist Essays on Virginia Woolf* (Lincoln, Nebr.: University of Nebraska Press, 1981).

—— (ed.), *Virginia Woolf: A Feminist Slant* (Lincoln, Nebr.: University of Nebraska Press, 1983).

—— *Virginia Woolf and the Languages of Patriarchy* (Bloomington, Ind.: Indiana University Press, 1987).

Marder, Herbert, *Virginia Woolf: Feminism and Art* (Chicago and London: University of Chicago Press, 1968).

Naremore, James, *The World Without a Self: Virginia Woolf and the Novel* (New Haven: Yale University Press, 1973).

Peach, Linden, *Virginia Woolf*, Critical Issues series (London and Basingstoke: Macmillan, 2000).

Phillips, Kathy J., *Virginia Woolf Against Empire* (Knoxville, Tenn.: University of Tennessee Press, 1994).

Richter, Harvena, *Virginia Woolf: The Inward Voyage* (Princeton: Princeton University Press, 1970).

Roe, Sue, *Writing and Gender: Virginia Woolf's Writing Practice* (Hemel Hempstead: Harvester Wheatsheaf, 1990).

—— and Sellers, Susan, *The Cambridge Companion to Virginia Woolf* (Cambridge: Cambridge University Press, 2000).

Snaith, Anna, *Virginia Woolf: Public and Private Negotiations* (London and Basingstoke: Macmillan, 2000).

Warner, Eric (ed.), *Virginia Woolf: A Centenary Perspective* (London and Basingstoke: Macmillan, 1984).

Zwerdling, Alex, *Virginia Woolf and the Real World* (Berkeley, Los Angeles, and London: University of California Press, 1986).

Criticism of the Modernist Short Story and Woolf's Short Fiction

Allen, Walter, *The Short Story in English* (Oxford: Oxford University Press, 1981).

Baldwin, Dean R., *Virginia Woolf: A Study of the Short Fiction* (Boston, Mass.: Twayne, 1989).

Bayley, John, *The Short Story: Henry James to Elizabeth Bowen* (Brighton: Harvester Press, 1988).

Fleishman, Avrom, 'Forms of the Woolfian Short Story', in Ralph Freedman (ed.), *Virginia Woolf: Revaluation and Continuity* (Berkeley, Los Angeles, and London: University of California Press, 1980), 44–70.

Flora, Joseph M. (ed.), *The English Short Story 1880–1945: A Critical History* (Boston, Mass.: Twayne, 1985).

Hanson, Clare, *Short Stories and Short Fictions, 1880–1980* (London and Basingstoke: Macmillan, 1985).

—— (ed.), *Re-reading the Short Story* (London and Basingstoke: Macmillan, 1989).

Head, Dominic, *The Modernist Short Story: A Study in Theory and Practice* (Cambridge: Cambridge University Press, 1992).

Shaw, Valerie, *The Short Story: A Critical Introduction* (London: Longman, 1983).

Stavely, Alice, ' "Kew Will Do": Cultivating Fictions of Kew Gardens', in Diane F. Gillespie and Leslie K. Hankins (eds.), *Virginia Woolf and the Sister Arts: Selected Papers from the Sixth Annual Conference on Virginia Woolf* (New York: Pace University Press, 1997), 57–66.

Further Reading in Oxford World's Classics

Joyce, James, *Dubliners*, ed. Jeri Johnson.

Mansfield, Katherine, *Selected Stories*, ed. Dan Davin.

Woolf, Virginia, *Between the Acts*, ed. Frank Kermode.

—— *Flush*, ed. Kate Flint.

—— *Jacob's Room*, ed. Kate Flint.

—— *Mrs Dalloway*, ed. David Bradshaw.

—— *Night and Day*, ed. Suzanne Raitt.

—— *Orlando: A Biography*, ed. Rachel Bowlby.

—— *A Room of One's Own* and *Three Guineas*, ed. Morag Shiach.

—— *To the Lighthouse*, ed. Margaret Drabble.

—— *The Voyage Out*, ed. Lorna Sage.

—— *The Waves*, ed. Gillian Beer.

—— *The Years*, ed. Hermione Lee.

A CHRONOLOGY OF VIRGINIA WOOLF

Life	*Historical and Cultural Background*
1882 (25 Jan.) Adeline Virginia Stephen (VW) born at 22 Hyde Park Gate, London.	Deaths of Darwin, Trollope, D. G. Rossetti; Joyce born; Stravinsky born; Married Women's Property Act; Society for Psychical Research founded.
1895 (5 May) Death of mother, Julia Stephen; VW's first breakdown occurs soon afterwards.	Death of T. H. Huxley; X-rays discovered; invention of the cinematograph; wireless telegraphy invented; arrest, trials, and conviction of Oscar Wilde. Wilde, *The Importance of Being Earnest* and *An Ideal Husband* Wells, *The Time Machine*
1896 (Nov.) Travels in France with sister Vanessa.	Death of William Morris; *Daily Mail* started. Hardy, *Jude the Obscure* Housman, *A Shropshire Lad*
1897 (10 April) Marriage of half-sister Stella; (19 July) death of Stella; (Nov.) VW learning Greek and History at King's College, London.	Queen Victoria's Diamond Jubilee; Tate Gallery opens. Stoker, *Dracula* James, *What Maisie Knew*
1898	Deaths of Gladstone and Lewis Carroll; radium and plutonium discovered. Wells, *The War of the Worlds*
1899 (30 Oct.) VW's brother Thoby goes up to Trinity College, Cambridge, where he forms friendships with Lytton Strachey, Leonard Woolf, Clive Bell, and others of the future Bloomsbury Group (VW's younger brother Adrian follows him to Trinity in 1902).	Boer War begins. Births of Bowen and Coward. Symons, *The Symbolist Movement in Literature* James, *The Awkward Age* Freud, *The Interpretation of Dreams*
1900	Deaths of Nietzsche, Wilde, and Ruskin; *Daily Express* started; Planck announces quantum theory; Boxer Rising. Conrad, *Lord Jim*

1901		Death of Queen Victoria; accession of Edward VII; first wireless communication between Europe and USA; 'World's Classics' series begun.
		Kipling, *Kim*
1902	VW starts private lessons in Greek with Janet Case.	End of Boer War; British Academy founded; *Encyclopaedia Britannica* (10th edn.); *TLS* started.
		Bennett, *Anna of the Five Towns*
		James, *The Wings of the Dove*
1903		Deaths of Gissing and Spencer; *Daily Mirror* started; Wright brothers make their first aeroplane flight; Emmeline Pankhurst founds Women's Social and Political Union.
		Butler, *The Way of All Flesh*
		James, *The Ambassadors*
		Moore, *Principia Ethica*
1904	(22 Feb.) Death of father, Sir Leslie Stephen. In spring, VW travels to Italy with Vanessa and friend Violet Dickinson. (10 May) VW has second nervous breakdown and is ill for three months. Moves to 46 Gordon Square. (14 Dec.) VW's first publication appears.	Deaths of Christina Rossetti and Chekhov; Russo-Japanese War; *Entente Cordiale* between Britain and France.
		Chesterton, *The Napoleon of Notting Hill*
		Conrad, *Nostromo*
		James, *The Golden Bowl*
1905	(March, April) Travels in Portugal and Spain. Writes reviews and teaches once a week at Morley College, London.	Einstein, *Special Theory of Relativity*; Sartre born.
		Shaw, *Major Barbara* and *Man and Superman*
		Wells, *Kipps*
		Forster, *Where Angels Fear to Tread*
1906	(Sept. and Oct.) Travels in Greece. (20 Nov.) Death of Thoby Stephen.	Death of Ibsen; Beckett born; Liberal Government elected; Campbell-Bannerman Prime Minister; launch of HMS *Dreadnought*.
1907	(7 Feb.) Marriage of Vanessa to Clive Bell. VW moves with Adrian to 29 Fitzroy Square. At work on her first novel, 'Melymbrosia' (working title for *The Voyage Out*).	Auden born; Anglo-Russian Entente.
		Synge, *The Playboy of the Western World*
		Conrad, *The Secret Agent*
		Forster, *The Longest Journey*

1908	(Sept.) Visits Italy with the Bells.	Asquith Prime Minister; Old Age Pensions Act; Elgar's First Symphony. Bennett, *The Old Wives' Tale* Forster, *A Room with a View* Chesterton, *The Man Who Was Thursday*
1909	(17 Feb.) Lytton Strachey proposes marriage. (30 March) First meets Lady Ottoline Morrell. (April) Visits Florence. (Aug.) Visits Bayreuth and Dresden.	Death of Meredith; 'People's Budget'; English Channel flown by Blériot. Wells, *Tono-Bungay* Masterman, *The Condition of England* Marinetti, *Futurist Manifesto*
1910	(Jan.) Works for women's suffrage. (June-Aug.) Spends time in a nursing home at Twickenham.	Deaths of Edward VII, Tolstoy, and Florence Nightingale; accession of George V; *Encyclopaedia Britannica* (11th edn.); Roger Fry's Post-Impressionist Exhibition. Bennett, *Clayhanger* Forster, *Howard's End* Yeats, *The Green Helmet* Wells, *The History of Mr Polly*
1911	(April) Travels to Turkey, where Vanessa is ill. (Nov.) Moves to 38 Brunswick Square, sharing house with Adrian, John Maynard Keynes, Duncan Grant, and Leonard Woolf.	National Insurance Act; Suffragette riots. Conrad, *Under Western Eyes* Wells, *The New Machiavelli* Lawrence, *The White Peacock*
1912	Rents Asheham House. (Feb.) Spends some days in Twickenham nursing home. (10 Aug.) Marriage to Leonard Woolf. Honeymoon in Provence, Spain, and Italy. (Oct.) Moves to 13 Clifford's Inn, London.	Second Post-Impressionist Exhibition; Suffragettes active; strikes by dockers, coal-miners, and transport workers; Irish Home Rule Bill rejected by Lords; sinking of SS *Titanic*; death of Scott in the Antarctic; *Daily Herald* started. English translations of Chekhov and Dostoevsky begin to appear.
1913	(March) MS of *The Voyage Out* delivered to publisher. Unwell most of summer. (9 Sept.) Suicide attempt. Remains under care of nurses and husband for rest of year.	*New Statesman* started; Suffragettes active. Lawrence, *Sons and Lovers*

1914	(16 Feb.) Last nurse leaves. Moves to Richmond, Surrey.	Irish Home Rule Bill passed by Parliament; First World War begins (4 Aug.); Dylan Thomas born. Lewis, *Blast* Joyce, *Dubliners* Yeats, *Responsibilities* Hardy, *Satires of Circumstance* Bell, *Art*
1915	Purchase of Hogarth House, Richmond. (26 March) *The Voyage Out* published. (April, May) Bout of violent madness; under care of nurses until November.	Death of Rupert Brooke; Einstein, *General Theory of Relativity*; Second Battle of Ypres; Dardanelles Campaign; sinking of SS *Lusitania*; air attacks on London. Ford, *The Good Soldier* Lawrence, *The Rainbow* Brooke, *1914 and Other Poems* Richardson, *Pointed Roofs*
1916	(17 Oct.) Lectures to Richmond branch of the Women's Co-operative Guild. Regular work for *TLS*.	Death of James; Lloyd George Prime Minister; First Battle of the Somme; Battle of Verdun; Gallipoli Campaign; Easter Rising in Dublin. Joyce, *Portrait of the Artist as a Young Man*
1917	(July) Hogarth Press commences publication with 'The Mark on the Wall' and a story by Leonard Woolf. VW begins work on *Night and Day*.	Death of Edward Thomas. Third Battle of Ypres (Passchendaele); T.E. Lawrence's campaigns in Arabia; USA enters the War; Revolution in Russia (Feb., Oct.); Balfour Declaration. Eliot, *Prufrock and Other Observations*
1918	Writes reviews and *Night and Day*; also sets type for the Hogarth Press. (15 Nov.) First meets T. S. Eliot.	Death of Owen; Second Battle of the Somme; final German offensive collapses; Armistice with Germany (11 Nov.); Franchise Act grants vote to women over 30; influenza pandemic kills millions. Lewis, *Tarr* Hopkins, *Poems* Strachey, *Eminent Victorians*
1919	(1 July) Purchase of Monk's House, Rodmell, Sussex. (20 Oct.) *Night and Day* published.	Treaty of Versailles; Alcock and Brown fly the Atlantic; National Socialists founded in Germany. Sinclair, *Mary Olivier* Shaw, *Heartbreak House*
1920	Works on journalism and *Jacob's Room*.	League of Nations established. Pound, *Hugh Selwyn Mauberley* Lawrence, *Women in Love* Eliot, *The Sacred Wood* Fry, *Vision and Design*

1921	(7 or 8 April) *Monday or Tuesday* published. Ill for summer months. (4 Nov.) Finishes *Jacob's Room*.	Irish Free State founded. Huxley, *Crome Yellow*
1922	(Jan. to May) Ill. (14 Dec.) First meets Vita Sackville-West. (24 Oct.) *Jacob's Room* published.	Bonar Law Prime Minister; Mussolini forms Fascist Government in Italy; death of Proust; *Encyclopaedia Britannica* (12th edn.); *Criterion* founded; BBC founded; Irish Free State proclaimed. Eliot, *The Waste Land* Galsworthy, *The Forsyte Saga* Joyce, *Ulysses* Mansfield, *The Garden Party* Wittgenstein, *Tractatus Logico-Philosophicus*
1923	(March, April) Visits Spain. Works on 'The Hours', the first version of *Mrs Dalloway*.	Baldwin Prime Minister; BBC radio begins broadcasting (Nov.); death of K. Mansfield.
1924	Purchase of lease on 52 Tavistock Square, Bloomsbury. Gives lecture that becomes 'Mr Bennett and Mrs Brown'. (8 Oct.) Finishes *Mrs Dalloway*.	First (minority) Labour Government; Ramsay MacDonald Prime Minister; deaths of Lenin, Kafka, and Conrad. Ford, *Some Do Not* Forster, *A Passage to India* O'Casey, *Juno and the Paycock* Coward, *The Vortex*
1925	(23 April) *The Common Reader* published. (14 May) *Mrs Dalloway* published. Ill during summer.	Gerhardie, *The Polyglots* Ford, *No More Parades* Huxley, *Those Barren Leaves* Whitehead, *Science and the Modern World*
1926	(Jan) Unwell with German measles. Writes *To the Lighthouse*.	General Strike (3–12 May); *Encyclopaedia Britannica* (13th edn.); first television demonstration. Ford, *A Man Could Stand Up* Tawney, *Religion and the Rise of Capitalism*
1927	(March, April) Travels in France and Italy. (5 May) *To the Lighthouse* published. (5 Oct.) Begins *Orlando*.	Lindburgh flies solo across the Atlantic; first 'talkie' films.
1928	(11 Oct.) *Orlando* published. Delivers lectures at Cambridge on which she bases *A Room of One's Own*.	Death of Hardy; votes for women over 21. Yeats, *The Tower* Lawrence, *Lady Chatterley's Lover* Waugh, *Decline and Fall* Sherriff, *Journey's End* Ford, *Last Post* Huxley, *Point Counter Point* Bell, *Civilization*

1929	(Jan.) Travels to Berlin. (24 Oct.) *A Room of One's Own* published.	2nd Labour Government, MacDonald Prime Minister; collapse of New York Stock Exchange; start of world economic depression. Graves, *Goodbye to All That* Aldington, *Death of a Hero* Green, *Living*
1930	(20 Feb.) First meets Ethel Smyth; (29 May) Finishes first version of *The Waves*.	Mass unemployment; television starts in USA; deaths of Lawrence and Conan Doyle. Auden, *Poems* Eliot, *Ash Wednesday* Waugh, *Vile Bodies* Coward, *Private Lives* Lewis, *Apes of God*
1931	(April) Car tour through France. (8 Oct.) *The Waves* published. Writes *Flush*.	Formation of National Government; abandonment of Gold Standard; death of Bennett; Japan invades China.
1932	(21 Jan.) Death of Lytton Strachey. (13 Oct.) *The Common Reader*, 2nd series, published. Begins *The Years*, at this point called 'The Pargiters'.	Roosevelt becomes President of USA; hunger marches start in Britain; *Scrutiny* starts. Huxley, *Brave New World*
1933	(May) Car tour of France and Italy. (5 Oct.) *Flush* published.	Deaths of Galsworthy and George Moore; Hitler becomes Chancellor of Germany. Orwell, *Down and Out in Paris and London* Wells, *The Shape of Things to Come*
1934	Works on *The Years*. (9 Sept.) Death of Roger Fry.	Waugh, *A Handful of Dust* Graves, *I, Claudius* Beckett, *More Pricks than Kicks* Toynbee, *A Study of History*
1935	Rewrites *The Years*. (May) Car tour of Holland, Germany, and Italy.	George V's Silver Jubilee; Baldwin Prime Minister of National Government; Germany re-arms; Italian invasion of Abyssinia (Ethiopia). Isherwood, *Mr Norris Changes Trains* T. S. Eliot, *Murder in the Cathedral*
1936	(May–Oct.) Ill. Finishes *The Years*. Begins *Three Guineas*.	Death of George V; accession of Edward VIII; abdication crisis; accession of George VI; Civil War breaks out in Spain; first of the Moscow show trials; Germany re-occupies the Rhineland; BBC television begins (2 Nov); deaths of Chesterton, Kipling, and Houseman. Orwell, *Keep the Aspidistra Flying*

1937	(15 March) *The Years* published. Begins *Roger Fry: A Biography*. (18 July) Death in Spanish Civil War of Julian Bell, son of Vanessa.	Chamberlain Prime Minister; destruction of Guernica; death of Barrie. Orwell, *The Road to Wigan Pier*
1938	(2 June) *Three Guineas* published. Works on *Roger Fry*, and begins to envisage *Between the Acts*.	German *Anschluss* with Austria; Munich agreement; dismemberment of Czechoslovakia; first jet engine. Beckett, *Murphy* Bowen, *The Death of the Heart* Greene, *Brighton Rock*
1939	VW moves to 37 Mecklenburgh Square, but lives mostly at Monk's House. Works on *Between the Acts*. Meets Freud in London.	End of Civil War in Spain; Russo–German pact; Germany invades Poland (Sept.); Britain and France declare war on Germany (3 Sept.); deaths of Freud, Yeats, and Ford. Joyce, *Finnegan's Wake* Isherwood, *Goodbye to Berlin*
1940	(25 July) *Roger Fry* published. (10 Sept.) Mecklenburgh Square house bombed. (18 Oct.) Witnesses the ruins of 52 Tavistock Square, destroyed by bombs. (23 Nov.) Finishes *Between the Acts*.	Germany invades north-west Europe; fall of France; evacuation of British troops from Dunkirk; Battle of Britain; beginning of 'the Blitz'; National Government under Churchill.
1941	(26 Feb.) Revises *Between the Acts*. Becomes ill. (28 March) Drowns herself in River Ouse, near Monk's House. (July) *Between the Acts* published.	Germany invades USSR; Japanese destroy US Fleet at Pearl Harbor; USA enters war; death of Joyce.

THE MARK ON THE WALL AND
OTHER SHORT FICTION

THE MARK ON THE WALL

PERHAPS it was the middle of January in the present year that I first looked up and saw the mark on the wall. In order to fix a date it is necessary to remember what one saw. So now I think of the fire; the steady film of yellow light upon the page of my book; the three chrysanthemums in the round glass bowl on the mantelpiece. Yes, it must have been the winter time, and we had just finished our tea, for I remember that I was smoking a cigarette when I looked up and saw the mark on the wall for the first time. I looked up through the smoke of my cigarette and my eye lodged for a moment upon the burning coals, and that old fancy of the crimson flag flapping from the castle tower came into my mind, and I thought of the cavalcade of red knights riding up the side of the black rock. Rather to my relief the sight of the mark interrupted the fancy, for it is an old fancy, an automatic fancy, made as a child perhaps. The mark was a small round mark, black upon the white wall, about six or seven inches above the mantelpiece.

How readily our thoughts swarm upon a new object, lifting it a little way, as ants carry a blade of straw so feverishly, and then leave it . . . If that mark was made by a nail, it can't have been for a picture, it must have been for a miniature—the miniature of a lady with white powdered curls, powder-dusted cheeks, and lips like red carnations. A fraud of course, for the people who had this house before us would have chosen pictures in that way—an old picture for an old room. That is the sort of people they were— very interesting people, and I think of them so often, in such queer places, because one will never see them again, never know what happened next. They wanted to leave this house because they wanted to change their style of furniture, so he said, and he was in process of saying that in his opinion art should have ideas behind it when we were torn asunder, as one is torn from the old lady about to pour out tea and the young man about to hit the tennis ball in the back garden of the suburban villa as one rushes past in the train.

But as for that mark, I'm not sure about it; I don't believe it was made by a nail after all; it's too big, too round, for that. I might get up, but if I got up and looked at it, ten to one I shouldn't be able to say for certain; because once a thing's done, no one ever knows how it happened. O dear me, the mystery of life! The inaccuracy of thought! The ignorance of humanity! To show very little control of our possessions we have—what an accidental affair this living is after all our civilization—let me just count over a few of the things lost in one lifetime, beginning, for that seems always the most mysterious of losses—what cat would gnaw, what rat would nibble—three pale blue canisters of book-binding tools? Then there were the bird cages, the iron hoops, the steel skates, the Queen Anne coal-scuttle, the bagatelle board, the hand organ—all gone, and jewels too. Opals and emeralds, they lie about the roots of turnips. What a scraping paring affair it is to be sure! The wonder is that I've any clothes on my back, that I sit surrounded by solid furniture at this moment. Why, if one wants to compare life to anything, one must liken it to being blown through the Tube at fifty miles an hour—landing at the other end without a single hairpin in one's hair! Shot out at the feet of God entirely naked! Tumbling head over heels in the asphodel meadows* like brown paper parcels pitched down a shoot in the post office! With one's hair flying back like the tail of a racehorse. Yes, that seems to express the rapidity of life, the perpetual waste and repair; all so casual, all so haphazard . . .

But after life. The slow pulling down of thick green stalks so that the cup of the flower, as it turns over, deluges one with purple and red light. Why, after all, should one not be born there as one is born here, helpless, speechless, unable to focus one's eyesight, groping at the roots of the grass, at the toes of the Giants? As for saying which are trees, and which are men and women, or whether there are such things, that one won't be in a condition to do for fifty years or so. There will be nothing but spaces of light and dark, intersected by thick stalks, and rather higher up perhaps, rose-shaped blots of an indistinct colour—dim pinks and blues—which will, as times goes on, become more definite, become—I don't know what . . .

And yet that mark on the wall is not a hole at all. It may even be caused by some round black substance, such as a small rose leaf, left over from the summer, and I, not being a very vigilant housekeeper—look at the dust on the mantelpiece, for example, the dust which, so they say, buried Troy three times over,* only fragments of pots utterly refusing annihilation, as one can believe.

The tree outside the window taps very gently on the pane . . . I want to think quietly, calmly, spaciously, never to be interrupted, never to have to rise from my chair, to slip easily from one thing to another, without any sense of hostility, or obstacle. I want to sink deeper and deeper, away from the surface, with its hard separate facts. To steady myself, let me catch hold of the first idea that passes . . . Shakespeare . . . Well, he will do as well as another. A man who sat himself solidly in an armchair, and looked into the fire, so—A shower of ideas fell perpetually from some very high Heaven down through his mind. He leant his forehead on his hand, and people, looking in through the open door—for this scene is supposed to take place on a summer's evening—But how dull this is, this historical fiction! It doesn't interest me at all. I wish I could hit upon a pleasant track of thought, a track indirectly reflecting credit upon myself, for those are the pleasantest thoughts, and very frequent even in the minds of modest mouse-coloured people, who believe genuinely that they dislike to hear their own praises. They are not thoughts directly praising oneself; that is the beauty of them; they are thoughts like this:

'And then I came into the room. They were discussing botany. I said how I'd seen a flower growing on a dust heap on the site of an old house in Kingsway. The seed, I said, must have been sown in the reign of Charles the First.* What flowers grew in the reign of Charles the First' I asked—(but I don't remember the answer). Tall flowers with purple tassels to them perhaps.* And so it goes on. All the time I'm dressing up the figure of myself in my own mind, lovingly, stealthily, not openly adoring it, for if I did that, I should catch myself out, and stretch my hand at once for a book in self-protection. Indeed, it is curious how instinctively one protects the image of oneself from idolatry or any other handling that could make it ridiculous, or too unlike the original to be believed in any longer. Or is it not so very curious after all? It is a matter of great importance. Suppose the looking-glass smashes, the image disappears, and the romantic figure with the green of forest depths all about it is there no longer, but only that shell of a person which is seen by other people—what an airless, shallow, bald, prominent world it becomes! A world not to be lived in. As we face each other in omnibuses and underground railways we are looking into the mirror; that accounts for the vagueness, the gleam of glassiness, in our eyes. And the novelists in future will realize more and more the importance of these reflections, for of course there is not one reflection but an almost infinite number; those are the depths they will explore, those the phantoms they will pursue, leaving the description of reality more and more out of their stories, taking a knowledge of it for granted, as the Greeks did and Shakespeare perhaps—but these generalizations are very worthless. The military sound of the word is enough. It recalls leading articles, cabinet ministers—a whole class of things indeed which as a child one thought the thing itself, the standard thing, the real thing, from which one could not depart save at the risk of nameless damnation. Generalizations bring back somehow Sunday in London, Sunday afternoon walks, Sunday luncheons, and also ways of speaking of the dead, clothes, and habits—like the habit of sitting all together in one room until a certain hour, although nobody liked it. There was a rule for everything. The rule for tablecloths at that particular period was that they should be made of tapestry with little yellow compartments marked upon them, such as you may see in photographs of the carpets in the corridors of the royal palaces. Tablecloths of a different kind were not real tablecloths. How shocking, and yet how wonderful it was to discover that these real things, Sunday luncheons, Sunday walks, country houses, and tablecloths were not entirely real, were indeed half phantoms, and the damnation which visited the disbeliever in them was only a sense of illegitimate freedom. What now takes the place of those things I wonder, those real standard things? Men perhaps, should you be a woman; the masculine point of view which governs our lives, which sets the standard, which establishes Whitaker's Table of Precedency, which has become, I suppose, since the war half a phantom to many men and women, which soon, one may hope, will be laughed into the dustbin where the phantoms go, the mahogany sideboards and the Landseer prints,* Gods and Devils, Hell and so forth, leaving us all with an intoxicating sense of illegitimate freedom—if freedom exists . . .

In certain lights that mark on the wall seems actually to project from the wall. Nor is it entirely circular. I cannot be sure, but it seems to cast a perceptible shadow, suggesting that if I ran my finger down that strip of the wall it would, at a certain point, mount and descend a small tumulus, a smooth tumulus like those barrows on the South Downs* which are, they say, either tombs or camps. Of the two I should prefer them to be tombs, desiring melancholy like most English people, and finding it natural at the end of a walk to think of the bones stretched beneath the turf . . . There must be some book about it. Some antiquary must have dug up those bones and given them a name . . . What sort of a man is an antiquary, I wonder? Retired Colonels for the most part, I daresay, leading parties of aged labourers to the top here, examining clods of earth and stone, and getting into correspondence with the neighbouring clergy, which, being opened at breakfast time, gives them a feeling of importance, and the comparison of arrow-heads necessitates cross-country journeys to the country towns, an agreeable necessity both to them and to their elderly wives, who wish to make plum jam or to clean out the study, and have every reason for keeping that great question of the camp or the tomb in perpetual suspension, while the Colonel himself feels agreeably philosophic in accumulating evidence on both sides of the question. It is true that he does finally incline to believe in the camp; and, being opposed, indites a pamphlet which he is about to read at the quarterly meeting of the local society when a stroke lays him low, and his last conscious thoughts are not of wife or child, but of the camp and that arrow-head there, which is now in the case at the local museum, together with the foot of a Chinese murderess, a handful of Elizabethan nails, a great many Tudor clay pipes, a piece of Roman pottery, and the wine-glass that Nelson drank out of—proving I really don't know what.

No, no, nothing is proved, nothing is known. And if I were to get up at this very moment and ascertain that the mark on the wall is really—what shall we say?—the head of a gigantic old nail, driven in two hundred years ago, which has now, owing to the patient attrition of many generations of housemaids, revealed its head above the coat of paint; and is taking its first view of modern life in the sight of a white-walled fire-lit room, what should I gain?—Knowledge? Matter for further speculation? I can think sitting still as well as standing up. And what is knowledge? What are our learned men save the descendants of witches and hermits who crouched in caves and in woods brewing herbs, interrogating shrew-mice and writing down the language of the stars? And the less we honour them as our superstitions dwindle and our respect for beauty and health of mind increases ... Yes, one could imagine a very pleasant world. A quiet spacious world, with the flowers so red and blue in the open fields. A world without professors or specialists or housekeepers with the profiles of policemen, a world which one could slice with one's thought as a fish slices the water with his fin, grazing the stems of the water lilies, hanging suspended over nests of white sea eggs ... How peaceful it is down here, rooted in the centre of the world and gazing up through the gray waters, with their sudden gleams of light, and their reflections—If it were not for Whitaker's Almanack—if it were not for the Table of Precedency!

I must jump up and see for myself what that mark on the wall really is—a nail, a rose-leaf, a crack in the wood?

Here is Nature once more at her old game of self-preservation. This train of thought, she perceives, is threatening mere waste of energy, even some collision with reality, for who will ever be able to lift a finger against Whitaker's Table of Precedency? The Archbishop of Canterbury is followed by the Lord High Chancellor; the Lord High Chancellor is followed by the Archbishop of York. Everybody follows somebody, such is the philosophy of Whitaker; and the great thing is to know who follows whom. Whitaker knows, and let that, so Nature counsels, comfort you, instead of enraging you; and if you can't be comforted, if you must shatter this hour of peace, think of the mark on the wall.

I understand Nature's game—her prompting to take action as a way of ending any thought that threatens to excite or to pain. Hence, I suppose, comes our slight contempt for men of action—men, we assume, who don't think. Still, there's no harm in putting a full stop to one's disagreeable thoughts by looking at a mark on the wall.

Indeed, now that I have fixed my eyes upon it, I feel that I have grasped a plank in the sea; I feel a satisfying sense of reality which at once turns the two Archbishops and the Lord High Chancellor to the shadows of shades. Here is something definite, something real. Thus, waking from a midnight dream of horror, one hastily turns on the light and lies quiescent, worshipping the chest of drawers, worshipping solidity, worshipping reality, worshipping the impersonal world which is a proof of some existence other than ours. That is what one wants to be sure of . . . Wood is a pleasant thing to think about. It comes from a tree; and trees grow, and we don't know how they grow. For years and years they grow, without paying any attention to us, in meadows, in forests, and by the side of rivers—all things one likes to think about. The cows swish their tails beneath them on hot afternoons; they paint rivers so green that when a moorhen dives one expects to see its feathers all green when it comes up again. I like to think of the fish balanced against the stream like flags blown out; and of water-beetles slowly raising domes of mud upon the bed of the river. I like to think of the tree itself: first the close dry sensation of being wood; then the grinding of the storm; then the slow, delicious ooze of sap. I like to think of it, too, on winter's nights standing in the empty field with all leaves close-furled, nothing tender exposed to the iron bullets of the moon, a naked mast upon an earth that goes tumbling, tumbling, all night long. The song of birds must sound very loud and strange in June; and how cold the feet of insects must feel upon it, as they make laborious progresses up the creases of the bark, or sun themselves upon the thin green awning of the leaves, and look straight in front of them with diamond-cut red eyes . . . One by one the fibres snap beneath the immense cold pressure of the earth, then the last storm comes and, falling, the highest branches drive deep into the ground again. Even so, life isn't done with; there are a million patient, watchful lives still for a tree, all over the world, in bedrooms, in ships, on the pavement, lining rooms where men and women sit after tea, smoking cigarettes. It is full of peaceful thoughts, happy thoughts, this tree. I should like to take each one separately—but something is getting in the way . . . Where was I? What has it all been about? A tree? A river? The Downs? Whitaker's Almanack? The fields of asphodel? I can't remember a thing. Everything's moving, falling, slipping, vanishing . . . There is a vast upheaval of matter. Someone is standing over me and saying—

'I'm going out to buy a newspaper.'

'Yes?'

'Though it's no good buying newspapers . . . Nothing ever happens. Curse this war! God damn this war! . . . All the same, I don't see why we should have a snail on our wall.'

Ah, the mark on the wall! It was a snail.

KEW GARDENS

From the oval shaped flower-bed there rose perhaps a hundred stalks spreading into heart shaped or tongue shaped leaves half-way up and unfurling at the tip red or blue or yellow petals marked with spots of colour raised upon the surface; and from the red, blue or yellow gloom of the throat emerged a straight bar, rough with gold dust and slightly clubbed at the end.* The petals were voluminous enough to be stirred by the summer breeze, and when they moved, the red, blue and yellow lights passed one over the other, staining an inch of the brown earth beneath with a spot of the most intricate colour. The light fell either upon the smooth grey back of a pebble, or the shell of a snail with its brown circular veins, or, falling into a raindrop, it expanded with such intensity of red, blue and yellow the thin walls of water that one expected them to burst and disappear. Instead, the drop was left in a second silver grey once more, and the light now settled upon the flesh of a leaf, revealing the branching thread of fibre beneath the surface, and again it moved on and spread its illumination in the vast green spaces beneath the dome of the heart shaped and tongue shaped leaves. Then the breeze stirred rather more briskly overhead and the colour was flashed into the air above, into the eyes of the men and women who walk in Kew Gardens in July.

The figures of these men and women straggled past the flower-bed with a curiously irregular movement not unlike that of the white and blue butterflies who crossed the turf in zig-zag flights from bed to bed. The man was about six inches in front of the woman, strolling carelessly, while she bore on with greater purpose, only turning her head now and then to see that the children were not too far behind. The man kept this distance in front of the woman purposely, though perhaps unconsciously, for he wished to go on with his thoughts.

'Fifteen years ago I came here with Lily,' he thought. 'We sat somewhere over there by a lake, and I begged her to marry me all through the hot afternoon. How the dragonfly kept circling round us: how clearly I see the dragonfly and her shoe with the square silver buckle at the toe. All the time I spoke I saw her shoe and when it moved impatiently I knew without looking up what she was going to say: the whole of her seemed to be in her shoe. And my love, my desire, were in the dragonfly; for some reason I thought that if it settled there, on that leaf, the broad one with the red flower in the middle of it, if the dragonfly settled on the leaf she would say "Yes" at once. But the dragonfly went round and round: it never settled anywhere—of course not, happily not, or I shouldn't be walking here with Eleanor and the children—Tell me, Eleanor. D'you ever think of the past?'

'Why do you ask, Simon?'

'Because I've been thinking of the past. I've been thinking of Lily, the woman I might have married . . . Well, why are you silent? Do you mind my thinking of the past?'

'Why should I mind, Simon? Doesn't one always think of the past, in a garden with men and women lying under the trees? Aren't they one's past, all that remains of it, those men and women, those ghosts lying under the trees . . . one's happiness, one's reality?'

'For me, a square silver shoe buckle and a dragonfly—'

'For me, a kiss. Imagine six little girls sitting before their easels twenty years ago, down by the side of a lake, painting the water-lilies, the first red water-lilies I'd ever seen. And suddenly a kiss, there on the back of my neck. And my hand shook all the afternoon so that I couldn't paint. I took out my watch and marked the hour when I would allow myself to think of the kiss for five minutes only—it was so precious—the kiss of an old grey-haired woman with a wart on her nose, the mother of all my kisses all my life.* Come Caroline, come Hubert.'

They walked on past the flower-bed, now walking four abreast, and soon diminished in size among the trees and looked half transparent as the sunlight and shade swam over their backs in large trembling irregular patches.

In the oval flower-bed the snail, whose shell had been stained red, blue, and yellow for the space of two minutes or so, now appeared to be moving very slightly in its shell, and next began to

labour over the crumbs of loose earth which broke away and
rolled down as it passed over them. It appeared to have a definite
goal in front of it, differing in this respect from the singular high
stepping angular green insect who attempted to cross in front of
it, and waited for a second with its antennæ trembling as if in
deliberation, and then stepped off as rapidly and strangely in the
opposite direction. Brown cliffs with deep green lakes in the
hollows, flat bladelike trees that waved from root to tip, round
boulders of grey stone, vast crumpled surfaces of a thin crackling
texture—all these objects lay across the snail's progress between
one stalk and another to his goal. Before he had decided whether
to circumvent the arched tent of a dead leaf or to breast it there
came past the bed the feet of other human beings.

This time they were both men. The younger of the two wore
an expression of perhaps unnatural calm; he raised his eyes and
fixed them very steadily in front of him while his companion
spoke, and directly his companion had done speaking he looked
on the ground again and sometimes opened his lips only after a
long pause and sometimes did not open them at all. The elder
man had a curiously uneven and shaky method of walking, jerking his hand forward and throwing up his head abruptly, rather in
the manner of an impatient carriage horse tired of waiting outside
a house; but in the man these gestures were irresolute and pointless. He talked almost incessantly; he smiled to himself and again
began to talk, as if the smile had been an answer. He was talking
about spirits—the spirits of the dead, who, according to him,
were even now telling him all sorts of odd things about their
experiences in Heaven.

'Heaven was known to the ancients as Thessaly,* William, and
now, with this war, the spirit matter is rolling between the hills
like thunder.' He paused, seemed to listen, smiled, jerked his
head and continued—

'You have a small electric battery and a piece of rubber to
insulate the wire—isolate?—insulate?—well, we'll skip the
details, no good going into details that wouldn't be understood—
and in short the little machine stands in any convenient position
by the head of the bed, we will say, on a neat mahogany stand. All

arrangements being properly fixed by workmen under my direction, the widow applies her ear and summons the spirit by sign as agreed. Women! Widows! Women in black—'

Here he seemed to have caught sight of a woman's dress in the distance, which in the shade looked a purple black. He took off his hat, placed his hand upon his heart, and hurried towards her muttering and gesticulating feverishly. But William caught him by the sleeve and touched a flower with the tip of his walking-stick in order to divert the old man's attention. After looking at it for a moment in some confusion the old man bent his ear to it and seemed to answer a voice speaking from it, for he began talking about the forests of Uruguay which he had visited hundreds of years ago in company with the most beautiful young woman in Europe. He could be heard murmuring about forests of Uruguay blanketed with the wax petals of tropical roses, nightingales, sea beaches, mermaids, and women drowned at sea, as he suffered himself to be moved on by William, upon whose face the look of stoical patience grew slowly deeper and deeper.

Following his steps so closely as to be slightly puzzled by his gestures came two elderly women of the lower middle class, one stout and ponderous, the other rosy cheeked and nimble. Like most people of their station they were frankly fascinated by any signs of eccentricity betokening a disordered brain, especially in the well-to-do; but they were too far off to be certain whether the gestures were merely eccentric or genuinely mad. After they had scrutinised the old man's back in silence for a moment and given each other a queer, sly look, they went on energetically piecing together their very complicated dialogue:

'Nell, Bert, Lot, Cess, Phil, Pa, he says, I says, she says, I says, I says—'

'My Bert, Sis, Bill, Grandad, the old man, sugar,

> Sugar, flour, kippers, greens,
> Sugar, sugar, sugar.'

The ponderous woman looked through the pattern of falling words at the flowers standing cool, firm, and upright in the earth, with a curious expression. She saw them as a sleeper waking from a heavy sleep sees a brass candlestick reflecting the light in an unfamiliar way, and closes his eyes and opens them, and seeing the brass candlestick again, finally starts broad awake and stares at the candlestick with all his powers. So the heavy woman came to a standstill opposite the oval shaped flower-bed, and ceased even to pretend to listen to what the other woman was saying. She stood there letting the words fall over her, swaying the top part of her body slowly backwards and forwards, looking at the flowers. Then she suggested that they should find a seat and have their tea.

The snail had now considered every possible method of reaching his goal without going round the dead leaf or climbing over it. Let alone the effort needed for climbing a leaf, he was doubtful whether the thin texture which vibrated with such an alarming crackle when touched even by the tip of his horns would bear his weight; and this determined him finally to creep beneath it, for there was a point where the leaf curved high enough from the ground to admit him. He had just inserted his head in the opening and was taking stock of the high brown roof and was getting used to the cool brown light when two other people came past outside on the turf. This time they were both young, a young man and a young woman. They were both in the prime of youth, or even in that season which precedes the prime of youth, the season before the smooth pink folds of the flower have burst their gummy case, when the wings of the butterfly, though fully grown, are motionless in the sun.

'Lucky it isn't Friday,' he observed.

'Why? D'you believe in luck?'

'They make you pay sixpence on Friday.'

'What's sixpence anyway? Isn't it worth sixpence?'

'What's "it"—what do you mean by "it"?'

'O anything—I mean—you know what I mean.'

Long pauses came between each of these remarks; they were uttered in toneless and monotonous voices. The couple stood still on the edge of the flower-bed, and together pressed the end of her parasol deep down into the soft earth. The action and the fact that his hand rested on the top of hers expressed their feelings in a strange way, as these short insignificant words also expressed something, words with short wings for their heavy body of meaning, inadequate to carry them far and thus alighting awkwardly upon the very common objects that surrounded them, and were to their inexperienced touch so massive; but who knows (so they thought as they pressed the parasol into the earth) what precipices aren't concealed in them, or what slopes of ice don't shine in the sun on the other side? Who knows? Who has ever seen this before? Even when she wondered what sort of tea they gave you at Kew, he felt that something loomed up behind her words, and stood vast and solid behind them; and the mist very slowly rose and uncovered—O Heavens, what were those shapes?—little white tables, and waitresses who looked first at her and then at him; and there was a bill that he would pay with a real two shilling piece, and it was real, all real, he assured himself, fingering the coin in his pocket, real to everyone except to him and to her; even to him it began to seem real; and then—but it was too exciting to stand and think any longer, and he pulled the parasol out of the earth with a jerk and was impatient to find the place where one had tea with other people, like other people.

'Come along, Trissie; it's time we had our tea.'

'Wherever *does* one have one's tea?' she asked with the oddest thrill of excitement in her voice, looking vaguely round and letting herself be drawn on down the grass path, trailing her parasol, turning her head this way and that way, forgetting her tea, wishing to go down there and then down there, remembering orchids and cranes among wild flowers, a Chinese pagoda* and a crimson crested bird; but he bore her on.

Thus one couple after another with much the same irregular and aimless movement passed the flower-bed and were enveloped in layer after layer of green blue vapour, in which at first their bodies had substance and a dash of colour, but later both substance and colour dissolved in the green-blue atmosphere. How hot it was! So hot that even the thrush chose to hop, like a mechanical bird, in the shadow of the flowers, with long pauses between one movement and the next; instead of rambling vaguely the white butterflies danced one above another, making with their white shifting flakes the outline of a shattered marble column above the tallest flowers; the glass roofs of the palm house shone as if a whole market full of shiny green umbrellas had opened in the sun; and in the drone of the aeroplane the voice of the summer sky murmured its fierce soul. Yellow and black, pink and snow white, shapes of all these colours, men, women, and children were spotted for a second upon the horizon, and then, seeing the breadth of yellow that lay upon the grass, they wavered and sought shade beneath the trees, dissolving like drops of water in the yellow and green atmosphere, staining it faintly with red and blue. It seemed as if all gross and heavy bodies had sunk down in the heat motionless and lay huddled upon the ground, but their voices went wavering from them as if they were flames lolling from the thick waxen bodies of candles. Voices. Yes, voices. Wordless voices, breaking the silence suddenly with such depth of contentment, such passion of desire, or, in the voices of children, such freshness of surprise; breaking the silence? But there was no silence; all the time the motor omnibuses were turning their wheels and changing their gear; like a vast nest of Chinese boxes all of wrought steel turning ceaselessly one within another the city murmured; on the top of which the voices cried aloud and the petals of myriads of flowers flashed their colours into the air.

AN UNWRITTEN NOVEL

SUCH an expression of unhappiness was enough by itself to make one's eyes slide above the paper's edge to the poor woman's face—insignificant without that look, almost a symbol of human destiny with it. Life's what you see in people's eyes; life's what they learn, and, having learnt it, never, though they seek to hide it, cease to be aware of—what? That life's like that, it seems. Five faces opposite—five mature faces—and the knowledge in each face. Strange, though, how people want to conceal it! Marks of reticence are on all those faces: lips shut, eyes shaded, each one of the five doing something to hide or stultify his knowledge. One smokes; another reads; a third checks entries in a pocket book; a fourth stares at the map of the line framed opposite,* and the fifth—the terrible thing about the fifth is that she does nothing at all. She looks at life. Ah, but my poor, unfortunate woman, do play the game—do, for all our sakes, conceal it!

As if she heard me, she looked up, shifted slightly in her seat and sighed. She seemed to apologise and at the same time to say to me, 'if only you knew!' Then she looked at life again. 'But I do know,' I answered silently, glancing at *The Times* for manners' sake: 'I know the whole business. "Peace between Germany and the Allied Powers was yesterday officially ushered in at Paris— Signor Nitti, the Italian Prime Minister—a passenger train at Doncaster was in collision with a goods train . . . " We all know— *The Times* knows—but we pretend we don't.' My eyes had once more crept over the paper's rim. She shuddered, twitched her arm queerly to the middle of her back and shook her head. Again I dipped into my great reservoir of life. 'Take what you like,' I continued, 'births, deaths, marriages, Court Circular, the habits of birds, Leonardo da Vinci, the Sandhills murder, high wages and the cost of living—oh, take what you like,' I repeated, 'it's all in *The Times*!'* Again with infinite weariness she moved her head from side to side until, like a top exhausted with spinning, it settled on her neck.

The Times was no protection against such sorrow as hers. But other human beings forbade intercourse. The best thing to do against life was to fold the paper so that it made a perfect square, crisp, thick, impervious even to life. This done, I glanced up quickly, armed with a shield of my own. She pierced through my shield; she gazed into my eyes as if searching any sediment of courage at the depths of them and damping it to clay. Her twitch alone denied all hope, discounted all illusion.

So we rattled through Surrey and across the border into Sussex. But with my eyes upon life I did not see that the other travellers had left, one by one, till, save for the man who read, we were alone together. Here was Three Bridges station. We drew slowly down the platform and stopped. Was he going to leave us? I prayed both ways—I prayed last that he might stay. At that instant he roused himself, crumpled his paper contemptuously, like a thing done with, burst open the door and left us alone.

The unhappy woman, leaning a little forward, palely and colourlessly addressed me—talked of stations and holidays, of brothers at Eastbourne, and the time of year, which was, I forget now, early or late. But at last looking from the window and seeing, I knew, only life, she breathed, 'Staying away—that's the drawback of it—' Ah, now we approached the catastrophe, 'My sister-in-law'—the bitterness of her tone was like lemon on cold steel, and speaking, not to me, but to herself, she muttered, 'Nonsense, she would say—that's what they all say,' and while she spoke she fidgeted as though the skin on her back were as a plucked fowl's in a poulterer's shop-window.

'Oh that cow!' she broke off nervously, as though the great wooden cow in the meadow had shocked her and saved her from some indiscretion. Then she shuddered, and then she made the awkward angular movement that I had seen before, as if, after the spasm, some spot between the shoulders burnt or itched. Then again she looked the most unhappy woman in the world, and I once more reproached her, though not with the same conviction, for if there were a reason, and if I knew the reason, the stigma was removed from life.

'Sisters-in-law,' I said—

Her lips pursed as if to spit venom at the world; pursed they remained. All she did was to take her glove and rub hard at a spot on the window-pane. She rubbed as if she would rub something out for ever—some stain, some indelible contamination. Indeed, the spot remained for all her rubbing, and back she sank with the shudder and the clutch of the arm I had come to expect. Something impelled me to take my glove and rub my window. There, too, was a little speck on the glass. For all my rubbing it remained. And then the spasm went through me; I crooked my arm and plucked at the middle of my back. My skin, too, felt like the damp chicken's skin in the poulterer's shop-window; one spot between the shoulders itched and irritated, felt clammy, felt raw. Could I reach it? Surreptitiously I tried. She saw me. A smile of infinite irony, infinite sorrow, flitted and faded from her face. But she had communicated, shared her secret, passed her poison; she would speak no more. Leaning back in my corner, shielding my eyes from her eyes, seeing only the slopes and hollows, greys and purples, of the winter's landscape, I read her message, deciphered her secret, reading it beneath her gaze.

  Hilda's the sister-in-law. Hilda? Hilda? Hilda Marsh—Hilda the blooming, the full bosomed, the matronly. Hilda stands at the door as the cab draws up, holding a coin. 'Poor Minnie, more of a grasshopper than ever—old cloak she had last year. Well, well, with two children these days one can't do more. No, Minnie, I've got it; here you are, cabby—none of your ways with me. Come in, Minnie. Oh, I could carry *you*, let alone your basket!' So they go into the dining-room. 'Aunt Minnie, children.'

  Slowly the knives and forks sink from the upright. Down they get (Bob and Barbara), hold out hands stiffly; back again to their chairs, staring between the resumed mouthfuls. [But this we'll skip; ornaments, curtains, trefoil china plate, yellow oblongs of cheese, white squares of biscuit—skip—oh, but wait! Halfway through luncheon one of those shivers; Bob stares at her, spoon in mouth. 'Get on with your pudding, Bob;' but Hilda disapproves. 'Why *should* she twitch?' Skip, skip, till we reach the landing on the upper floor; stairs brass-bound; linoleum worn; oh yes! little bedroom looking out over the roofs of Eastbourne—zigzagging roofs like the spines of caterpillars, this way, that way, striped red and yellow, with blue-black slating]. Now, Minnie, the door's shut; Hilda heavily descends to the basement; you unstrap the straps of your basket, lay on the bed a meagre nightgown, stand side by side furred felt slippers. The looking-glass—no, you avoid the looking-glass. Some methodical disposition of hat-pins. Perhaps the shell box has something in it? You shake it; it's the pearl stud there was last year—that's all. And then the sniff, the sigh, the sitting by the window. Three o'clock on a December afternoon; the rain drizzling; one light low in the skylight of a drapery emporium; another high in a servant's bedroom—this one goes out. That gives her nothing to look at. A moment's blankness—then, what are you thinking? (Let me peep across at her opposite; she's asleep or pretending it; so what would she think about sitting at the window at three o'clock in the afternoon? Health, money, hills, her God?) Yes, sitting on the very edge of the chair looking over the roofs of Eastbourne, Minnie Marsh prays to God. That's all very well; and she may rub the pane too, as though to see God better; but what God does she see? Who's the God of Minnie Marsh, the God of the back streets of Eastbourne, the God of the three o'clock in the afternoon? I, too, see roofs, I see sky; but, oh, dear—this seeing of Gods! More like President Kruger than Prince Albert*—that's the best I can do for him; and I see him on a chair, in a black frock-coat, not so very high up either; I can manage a cloud or two for him to sit on; and then his hand trailing in the cloud holds a rod, a truncheon is it?—black, thick, thorned—a brutal old bully—Minnie's God! Did he send the itch and the patch and the twitch? Is that why she prays? What she rubs on the window is the stain of sin. Oh, she committed some crime!

I have my choice of crimes. The woods flit and fly—in summer there are bluebells; in the opening there, when spring comes, primroses. A parting, was it, twenty years ago? Vows broken? Not Minnie's! . . . She was faithful. How she nursed her mother! All her savings on the tombstone—wreaths under glass—daffodils in jars. But I'm off the track. A crime . . . They would say she kept her sorrow, suppressed her secret—her sex, they'd say—the scientific people. But what flummery to saddle *her* with sex! No—more like this. Passing down the streets of Croydon* twenty years ago, the violet loops of ribbon in the draper's window spangled in the electric light catch her eye. She lingers—past six. Still by running she can reach home. She pushes through the glass swing door. It's sale-time. Shallow trays brim with ribbons. She pauses, pulls this, fingers that with the raised roses on it—no need to choose, no need to buy, and each tray with its surprises. 'We don't shut till seven,' and then it *is* seven. She runs, she rushes, home she reaches, but too late. Neighbours—the doctor—baby brother—the kettle—scalded—hospital—dead—or only the shock of it, the blame? Ah, but the detail matters nothing! It's what she carries with her; the spot, the crime, the thing to expiate, always there between her shoulders. 'Yes,' she seems to nod to me, 'it's the thing I did.'

Whether you did, or what you did, I don't mind; it's not the thing I want. The draper's window looped with violet—that'll do; a little cheap perhaps, a little commonplace—since one has a choice of crimes, but then so many (let me peep across again—still sleeping, or pretending sleep! white, worn, the mouth closed—a touch of obstinacy, more than one would think—no hint of sex)—so many crimes aren't *your* crime; your crime was cheap; only the retribution solemn; for now the church door opens, the hard wooden pew receives her; on the brown tiles she kneels; every day, winter, summer, dusk, dawn (here she's at it) prays. All her sins fall, fall, for ever fall. The spot receives them. It's raised, it's red, it's burning. Next she twitches. Small boys point. 'Bob at lunch to-day'—But elderly women are the worst.

Indeed now you can't sit praying any longer. Kruger's sunk beneath the clouds—washed over as with a painter's brush of liquid grey, to which he adds a tinge of black—even the tip of the truncheon gone now. That's what always happens! Just as you've seen him, felt him, someone interrupts. It's Hilda now.

How you hate her! She'll even lock the bathroom door overnight, too, though it's only cold water you want, and sometimes when the night's been bad it seems as if washing helped. And John at breakfast—the children—meals are worst, and sometimes there are friends—ferns don't altogether hide 'em—they guess too; so out you go along the front, where the waves are grey, and the papers blow, and the glass shelters green and draughty, and the chairs cost tuppence—too much—for there must be preachers along the sands. Ah, that's a nigger—that's a funny man—that's a man with parakeets—poor little creatures! Is there no one here who thinks of God?—just up there, over the pier, with his rod—but no—there's nothing but grey in the sky or if it's blue the white clouds hide him, and the music—it's military music—and what are they fishing for? Do they catch them? How the children stare! Well, then home a back way—'Home a back way!' The words have meaning: might have been spoken by the old man with whiskers—no, no, he didn't really speak; but everything has meaning—placards leaning against doorways—names above shop-windows—red fruit in baskets—women's heads in the hairdresser's—all say 'Minnie Marsh!' But here's a jerk. 'Eggs are cheaper!' That's what always happens! I was heading her over the waterfall, straight for madness, when, like a flock of dream sheep, she turns t'other way and runs between my fingers. Eggs are cheaper. Tethered to the shores of the world, none of the crimes, sorrows, rhapsodies, or insanities for poor Minnie Marsh; never late for luncheon; never caught in a storm without a mackintosh; never utterly unconscious of the cheapness of eggs. So she reaches home—scrapes her boots.

Have I read you right? But the human face—the human face at the top of the fullest sheet of print holds more, withholds more. Now, eyes open, she looks out; and in the human eye—how d'you define it?—there's a break—a division—so that when you've grasped the stem the butterfly's off—the moth that hangs in the evening over the yellow flower—move, raise your hand, off, high, away. I won't raise my hand. Hang still, then, quiver, life, soul, spirit, whatever you are of Minnie Marsh—I, too, on my flower—the hawk over the down—alone, or what were the worth of life? To rise; hang still in the evening, in the midday; hang still over the down. The flicker of a hand—off, up! then poised again. Alone, unseen; seeing all so still down there, all so lovely. None seeing, none caring. The eyes of others our prisons; their thoughts our cages. Air above, air below. And the moon and immortality . . . Oh, but I drop to the turf! Are you down too, you in the corner, what's your name—woman—Minnie Marsh; some such name as that? There she is, tight to her blossom; opening her handbag, from which she takes a hollow shell—an egg—who was saying that eggs were cheaper? You or I? Oh, it was you who said it on the way home, you remember, when the old gentleman, suddenly opening his umbrella—or sneezing was it? Anyhow, Kruger went, and you came 'home a back way,' and scraped your boots. Yes. And now you lay across your knees a pocket-handkerchief into which drop little angular fragments of eggshell—fragments of a map—a puzzle. I wish I could piece them together! If you would only sit still. She's moved her knees—the map's in bits again. Down the slopes of the Andes the white blocks of marble go bounding and hurtling, crushing to death a whole troop of Spanish muleteers, with their convoy— Drake's booty, gold and silver,* But to return—

To what, to where? She opened the door, and, putting her umbrella in the stand—that goes without saying; so, too, the whiff of beef from the basement; dot, dot, dot. But what I cannot thus eliminate, what I must, head down, eyes shut, with the courage of a battalion and the blindness of a bull, charge and disperse are, indubitably, the figures behind the ferns, commercial travellers. There I've hidden them all this time in the hope that somehow they'd disappear, or better still emerge, as indeed they must, if the story's to go on gathering richness and rotundity, destiny and tragedy, as stories should, rolling along with it two, if not three, commercial travellers and a whole grove of aspidistra. 'The fronds of the aspidistra only partly concealed the commercial traveller—' Rhododendrons would conceal him utterly, and into the bargain give me my fling of red and white, for which I starve and strive; but rhododendrons in Eastbourne—in December— on the Marshes' table—no, no, I dare not; it's all a matter of crusts and cruets, frills and ferns. Perhaps there'll be a moment later by the sea. Moreover, I feel, pleasantly pricking through the green fretwork and over the glacis of cut glass, a desire to peer and peep at the man opposite—one's as much as I can manage.

James Moggridge is it, whom the Marshes call Jimmy? [Minnie you must promise not to twitch till I've got this straight] James Moggridge travels in—shall we say buttons?*—but the time's not come for bringing *them* in—the big and the little on the long cards, some peacock-eyed, others dull gold; cairngorms some, and others coral sprays—but I say the time's not come. He travels, and on Thursdays, his Eastbourne day, takes his meals with the Marshes. His red face, his little steady eyes—by no means altogether commonplace—his enormous appetite (that's safe; he won't look at Minnie till the bread's swamped the gravy dry), napkin tucked diamond-wise—but this is primitive, and, whatever it may do the reader, don't take me in. Let's dodge to the Moggridge household, set that in motion. Well, the family boots are mended on Sundays by James himself. He reads *Truth*.* But his passion? Roses—and his wife a retired hospital nurse—interesting—for God's sake let me have one woman with a name I like! But no; she's of the unborn children of the mind, illicit, none the less loved, like my rhododendrons. How many die in every novel that's written—the best, the dearest, while Moggridge lives. It's life's fault. Here's Minnie eating her egg at the moment opposite and at t'other end of the line—are we past Lewes?—there must be Jimmy—or what's her twitch for?

There must be Moggridge—life's fault. Life imposes her laws; life blocks the way—life's behind the fern; life's the tyrant; oh, but not the bully! No, for I assure you I come willingly; I come wooed by Heaven knows what compulsion across ferns and cruets, table splashed and bottles smeared. I come irresistibly to lodge myself somewhere on the firm flesh, in the robust spine, wherever I can penetrate or find foothold on the person, in the soul, of Moggridge the man. The enormous stability of the fabric; the spine tough as whalebone, straight as oak-tree; the ribs radiating branches; the flesh taut tarpaulin; the red hollows; the suck and regurgitation of the heart; while from above meat falls in brown cubes and beer gushes to be churned to blood again—and so we reach the eyes. Behind the aspidistra they see something: black, white, dismal; now the plate again; behind the aspidistra they see elderly women; 'Marsh's sister, Hilda's more my sort;' the tablecloth now. 'Marsh would know what's wrong with Morrises . . .' talk that over; cheese has come; the plate again; turn it round—the enormous fingers; now the woman opposite. 'Marsh's sister—not a bit like Marsh; wretched elderly female . . . You should feed your hens . . . God's truth, what's set her twitching? Not what *I* said? Dear, dear, dear! these elderly women. Dear, dear!'

[Yes, Minnie; I know you've twitched, but one moment—James Moggridge].

'Dear, dear, dear!' How beautiful the sound is! like the knock of a mallet on seasoned timber, like the throb of the heart of an ancient whaler when the seas press thick and the green is clouded. 'Dear, dear!' what a passing bell for the souls of the fretful to soothe them and solace them, lap them in linen, saying, 'So long. Good luck to you!' and then, 'What's your pleasure?' for though Moggridge would pluck his rose for her, that's done, that's over. Now what's the next thing? 'Madam, you'll miss your train,' for they don't linger.

That's the man's way; that's the sound that reverberates; that's St Paul's* and the motor-omnibuses. But we're brushing the crumbs off. Oh, Moggridge, you won't stay? You must be off? Are you driving through Eastbourne this afternoon in one of those little carriages? Are you the man who's walled up in green cardboard boxes, and sometimes has the blinds down, and some-times sits so solemn staring like a sphinx, and always there's a look of the sepulchral, something of the undertaker, the coffin, and the dusk about horse and driver? Do tell me—but the doors slammed. We shall never meet again. Moggridge, farewell!

Yes, yes, I'm coming. Right up to the top of the house. One moment I'll linger. How the mud goes round in the mind—what a swirl these monsters leave, the waters rocking, the weeds waving and green here, black there, striking to the sand, till by degrees the atoms reassemble, the deposit sifts itself, and again through the eyes one sees clear and still, and there comes to the lips some prayer for the departed, some obsequy for the souls of those one nods to, the people one never meets again.

James Moggridge is dead now, gone for ever. Well, Minnie—'I

can face it no longer.' If she said that—(Let me look at her. She is brushing the eggshell into deep declivities). She said it certainly, leaning against the wall of the bedroom, and plucking at the little balls which edge the claret-coloured curtain. But when the self speaks to the self, who is speaking?—the entombed soul, the spirit driven in, in, in to the central catacomb; the self that took the veil and left the world—a coward perhaps, yet somehow beautiful, as it flits with its lantern restlessly up and down the dark corridors. 'I can bear it no longer,' her spirit says. 'That man at lunch—Hilda—the children.' Oh, heavens, her sob! It's the spirit wailing its destiny, the spirit driven hither, thither, lodging on the diminishing carpets—meagre footholds—shrunken shreds of all the vanishing universe—love, life, faith, husband, children, I know not what splendours and pageantries glimpsed in girlhood. 'Not for me—not for me.'

But then—the muffins, the bald elderly dog? Bead mats I should fancy and the consolation of underlinen. If Minnie Marsh were run over and taken to hospital, nurses and doctors themselves would exclaim ... There's the vista and the vision— there's the distance—the blue blot at the end of the avenue, while, after all, the tea is rich, the muffin hot, and the dog—'Benny to your basket, sir, and see what mother's brought you!' So, taking the glove with the worn thumb, defying once more the encroaching demon of what's called going in holes, you renew the fortifications, threading the grey wool, running it in and out.

Running it in and out, across and over, spinning a web through which God himself—hush, don't think of God! How firm the stitches are! You must be proud of your darning. Let nothing disturb her. Let the light fall gently, and the clouds show an inner vest of the first green leaf. Let the sparrow perch on the twig and shake the raindrop hanging to the twig's elbow ... Why look up? Was it a sound, a thought? Oh, heavens! Back again to the thing you did, the plate glass with the violet loops? But Hilda will come. Ignominies, humiliations, oh! Close the breach.

Having mended her glove, Minnie Marsh lays it in the drawer. She shuts the drawer with decision. I catch sight of her face in the glass. Lips are pursed. Chin held high. Next she laces her shoes.

Then she touchs her throat. What's your brooch? Mistletoe or merry thought?* And what is happening? Unless I'm much mistaken, the pulse's quickened, the moments coming, the threads are racing, Niagara's ahead. Here's the crisis! Heaven be with you! Down she goes. Courage, courage! Face it, be it! For God's sake don't wait on the mat now! There's the door! I'm on your side. Speak! Confront her, confound her soul!

'Oh, I beg your pardon! Yes, this is Eastbourne. I'll reach it down for you. Let me try the handle.' [But, Minnie, though we keep up pretences, I've read you right—I'm with you now.]

'That's all your luggage?'

'Much obliged, I'm sure.'

(But why do you look about you? Hilda won't come to the station, nor John; and Moggridge is driving at the far side of Eastbourne.)

'I'll wait by my bag, ma'am, that's safest. He said he'd meet me . . . Oh, there he is! That's my son.'

So they walk off together.

Well, but I'm confounded . . . Surely Minnie, you know better! A strange young man . . . Stop! I'll tell him—Minnie!—Miss Marsh!—I don't know though. There's something queer in her cloak as it blows. Oh, but it's untrue, it's indecent . . . Look how he bends as they reach the gateway. She finds her ticket. What's the joke? Off they go, down the road, side by side . . . Well, my world's done for! What do I stand on? What do I know? That's not Minnie. There never was Moggridge. Who am I? Life's bare as bone.

And yet the last look of them—he stepping from the kerb and she following him round the edge of the big building brims me with wonder—floods me anew. Mysterious figures! Mother and son. Who are you? Why do you walk down the street? Where tonight will you sleep, and then, tomorrow? Oh, how it whirls and surges—floats me afresh! I start after them. People drive this way and that. The white light splutters and pours. Plate-glass windows. Carnations; chrysanthemums. Ivy in dark gardens. Milk carts at the door. Wherever I go, mysterious figures, I see you, turning the corner, mothers and sons; you, you, you. I hasten, I follow. This, I fancy, must be the sea. Grey is the landscape; dim as ashes; the water murmurs and moves. If I fall on my knees, if I go through the ritual, the ancient antics, it's you, unknown figures, you I adore; if I open my arms, it's you I embrace, you I draw to me—adorable world!

A HAUNTED HOUSE

Whatever hour you woke there was a door shutting. From room to room they went, hand in hand, lifting here, opening there, making sure—a ghostly couple.

'Here we left it,' she said. And he added, 'Oh, but here too!' 'It's upstairs,' she murmured. 'And in the garden,' he whispered. 'Quietly,' they said, 'or we shall wake them.'

But it wasn't that you woke us. Oh, no. 'They're looking for it; they're drawing the curtain' one might say, and so read on a page or two. 'Now they've found it,' one would be certain, stopping the pencil on the margin. And then, tired of réading, one might rise and see for oneself, the house all empty, the doors standing open, only the wood pigeons bubbling with content and the hum of the threshing machine sounding from the farm. 'What did I come in here for? What did I want to find?' My hands were empty. 'Perhaps it's upstairs then?' The apples were in the loft. And so down again, the garden still as ever, only the book had slipped into the grass.

But they had found it in the drawing-room. Not that one could ever see them. The window panes reflected apples, reflected roses; all the leaves were green in the glass. If they moved in the drawing-room, the apple only turned its yellow side. Yet, the moment after, if the door was opened, spread about the floor, hung upon the walls, pendant from the ceiling—what? My hands were empty. The shadow of a thrush crossed the carpet; from the deepest wells of silence the wood pigeon drew its bubble of sound. 'Safe, safe, safe,' the pulse of the house beat softly. 'The treasure buried; the room . . . ' the pulse stopped short. Oh, was that the buried treasure?

A moment later the light had faded. Out in the garden then? But the trees spun darkness for a wandering beam of sun. So fine, so rare, coolly sunk beneath the surface the beam I sought always burnt behind the glass. Death was the glass; death was between us; coming to the woman first, hundreds of years ago, leaving the house, sealing all the windows; the rooms were darkened. He left it, left her, went North, went East, saw the stars turned in the Southern sky; sought the house, found it dropped beneath the Downs.* 'Safe, safe, safe,' the pulse of the house beat gladly, 'The treasure yours.'

The wind roars up the avenue. Trees stoop and bend this way and that. Moonbeams splash and spill wildly in the rain. But the beam of the lamp falls straight from the window. The candle burns stiff and still. Wandering through the house, opening the windows, whispering not to wake us, the ghostly couple seek their joy.

'Here we slept,' she says. And he adds, 'Kisses without number.' 'Waking in the morning—' 'Silver between the trees—' 'Upstairs—' 'In the garden—' 'When summer came—' 'In winter snowtime—' The doors go shutting far in the distance, gently knocking like the pulse of a heart.

Nearer they come; cease at the doorway. The wind falls, the rain slides silver down the glass. Our eyes darken; we hear no steps beside us; we see no lady spread her ghostly cloak. His hands shield the lantern. 'Look,' he breathes. 'Sound asleep. Love upon their lips.'

Stooping, holding their silver lamp above us, long they look and deeply. Long they pause. The wind drives straightly; the flame stoops slightly. Wild beams of moonlight cross both floor and wall, and, meeting, stain the faces bent; the faces pondering; the faces that search the sleepers and seek their hidden joy.

'Safe, safe, safe,' the heart of the house beats proudly. 'Long years—' he sighs. 'Again you found me.' 'Here,' she murmurs, 'sleeping; in the garden reading; laughing, rolling apples in the loft. Here we left our treasure—' Stooping, their light lifts the lids upon my eyes. 'Safe! safe! safe!' the pulse of the house beats wildly. Waking, I cry 'Oh, is *this* your buried treasure? The light in the heart.'

MONDAY OR TUESDAY

LAZY and indifferent, shaking space easily from his wings, knowing his way, the heron passes over the church beneath the sky. White and distant, absorbed in itself, endlessly the sky covers and uncovers, moves and remains. A lake? Blot the shores of it out! A mountain? Oh, perfect—the sun gold on its slopes. Down that falls. Ferns then, or white feathers, for ever and ever—

Desiring truth, awaiting it, laboriously distilling a few words, for ever desiring—(a cry starts to the left, another to the right. Wheels strike divergently. Omnibuses conglomerate in conflict)—for ever desiring—(the clock asseverates with twelve distinct strokes that it is midday, light sheds gold scales; children swarm)—for ever desiring truth. Red is the dome; coins hang on the trees; smoke trails from the chimneys; bark, shout, cry 'Iron for sale'—and truth?

Radiating to a point men's feet and women's feet, black or gold-encrusted—(This foggy weather—Sugar? No, thank you—The commonwealth of the future)—the firelight darting and making the room red, save for the black figures and their bright eyes, while outside a van discharges, Miss Thingummy drinks tea at her desk, and plate-glass preserves fur coats—

Flaunted, leaf-light, drifting at corners, blown across the wheels, silver-splashed, home or not home, gathered, scattered, squandered in separate scales, swept up, down, torn, sunk, assembled*—and truth?

Now to recollect by the fireside on the white square of marble. From ivory depths words rising shed their blackness, blossom and penetrate. Fallen the book; in the flame, in the smoke, in the momentary sparks—or now voyaging, the marble square pendant, minarets beneath and the India seas, while space rushes blue and stars glint—truth? or now, content with closeness?

Lazy and indifferent the heron returns; the sky veils her stars; then bares them.

BLUE AND GREEN

Green

THE pointed fingers of glass hang downwards. The light slides down the glass, and drops a pool of green. All day long the ten fingers of the lustre* drop green upon the marble. The feathers of parakeets—their harsh cries—sharp blades of palm trees—green too; green needles glittering in the sun. But the hard glass drips on to the marble; the pools hover above the desert sand; the camels lurch through them; the pools settle on the marble; rushes edge them; weeds clog them; here and there a white blossom; the frog flops over; at night the stars are set there unbroken. Evening comes, and the shadow sweeps the green over the mantelpiece; the ruffled surface of ocean. No ships come; the aimless waves sway beneath the empty sky. It's night; the needles drip blots of blue. The green's out.

BLUE AND GREEN

Blue

THE snub-nosed monster rises to the surface and spouts through his blunt nostrils two columns of water, which, fiery-white in the centre, spray off into a fringe of blue beads. Strokes of blue line the black tarpaulin of his hide. Slushing the water through mouth and nostrils he sinks, heavy with water, and the blue closes over him dowsing the polished pebbles of his eyes. Thrown upon the beach he lies, blunt, obtuse, shedding dry blue scales. Their metallic blue stains the rusty iron on the beach. Blue are the ribs of the wrecked rowing boat. A wave rolls beneath the blue bells. But the cathedral's different, cold, incense laden, faint blue with the veils of madonnas.

THE STRING QUARTET

WELL, here we are, and if you cast your eye over the room you will see that Tubes and trams and omnibuses, private carriages not a few, even, I venture to believe, landaus with bays* in them, have been busy at it, weaving threads from one end of London to the other. Yet I begin to have my doubts—

If indeed it's true, as they're saying, that Regent Street is up, and the Treaty signed, and the weather not cold for the time of year, and even at that rent not a flat to be had, and the worst of influenza* is after effects; if I bethink me of having forgotten to write about the leak in the larder, and left my glove in the train; if the ties of blood require me, leaning forward, to accept cordially the hand which is perhaps offered hesitatingly—

'Seven years since we met!'

'The last time in Venice.'

'And where are you living now?'

'Well, the late afternoon suits me the best, though, if it weren't asking too much—'

'But I knew you at once!'

'Still, the war made a break—'

If the mind's shot through by such little arrows, and—for human society compels it—no sooner is one launched than another presses forward; if this engenders heat and in addition they've turned on the electric light; if saying one thing does, in so many cases, leave behind it a need to improve and revise, stirring besides regrets, pleasures, vanities, and desires—if it's all the facts I mean, and the hats, the fur boas, the gentlemen's swallow-tail coats, and pearl tie-pins that come to the surface—what chance is there?

Of what? It becomes every minute more difficult to say why, in spite of everything, I sit here believing I can't now say what, or even remember the last time it happened.

'Did you see the procession?'

'The King* looked cold.'

No, no, no. But what was it?

'She's bought a house at Malmesbury.'*

'How lucky to find one!'

On the contrary, it seems to me pretty sure that she, whoever she may be, is damned, since it's all a matter of flats and hats and sea gulls, or so it seems to be for a hundred people sitting here well dressed, walled in, furred, replete. Not that I can boast, since I too sit passive on a gilt chair, only turning the earth above a buried memory, as we all do, for there are signs, if I'm not mistaken, that we're all recalling something, furtively seeking something. Why fidget? Why so anxious about the sit of cloaks; and gloves—whether to button or unbutton? Then watch that elderly face against the dark canvas, a moment ago urbane and flushed; now taciturn and sad, as if in shadow. Was it the sound of the second violin tuning in the ante-room? Here they come; four black figures, carrying instruments, and seat themselves facing the white squares under the downpour of light; rest the tips of their bows on the music stand; with a simultaneous movement lift them; lightly poise them, and, looking across at the player opposite, the first violin counts one, two, three—

Flourish, spring, burgeon, burst! The pear tree on the top of the mountain. Fountains jet; drops descend. But the waters of the Rhone flow swift and deep, race under the arches, and sweep the trailing water leaves, washing shadows over the silver fish, the spotted fish rushed down by the swift waters, now swept into an eddy where—it's difficult this—conglomeration of fish all in a pool; leaping, splashing, scraping sharp fins; and such a boil of current that the yellow pebbles are churned round and round, round and round—free now, rushing downwards, or even some-how ascending in exquisite spirals into the air; curled like thin shavings from under a plane; up and up . . . How lovely goodness is in those who, stepping lightly, go smiling through the world! Also in old, jolly fishwives, squatted under arches, obscene old women, how deeply they laugh and shake and rollick, when they walk, from side to side, hum, hah!

'That's an early Mozart, of course—'

'But the tune, like all his tunes, makes one despair—I mean

hope. What do I mean? That's the worst of music! I want to dance, laugh, eat pink cakes, yellow cakes, drink thin, sharp wine. Or an indecent story, now—I could relish that. The older one grows the more one likes indecency. Hah, hah! I'm laughing. What at? You said nothing, nor did the old gentleman opposite . . . But suppose—suppose—Hush!'

The melancholy river bears us on. When the moon comes through the trailing willow boughs, I see your face, I hear your voice and the bird singing as we pass the osier bed. What are you whispering? Sorrow, sorrow. Joy, joy. Woven together like reeds in moonlight. Woven together, inextricably commingled, bound in pain and strewn in sorrow—crash!

The boat sinks. Rising, the figures ascend, but now leaf thin, tapering to a dusky wraith, which, fiery tipped, draws its twofold passion from my heart. For me it sings, unseals my sorrow, thaws compassion, floods with love the sunless world, nor ceasing, abates its tenderness but deftly, subtly, weaves in and out until in this pattern, this consummation, the cleft ones unify; soar, sob, sink to rest, sorrow and joy.

Why then grieve? Ask what? Remain unsatisfied? I say all's been settled; yes; laid to rest under a coverlet of rose leaves, falling. Falling. Ah, but they cease. One rose leaf, falling from an enormous height, like a little parachute dropped from an invisible balloon, turns, flutters waveringly. It won't reach us.

'No, no. I noticed nothing. That's the worst of music—these silly dreams. The second violin was late, you say?'

'There's old Mrs Munro, feeling her way out—blinder each year, poor woman—on this slippery floor.'

Eyeless old age, grey-headed Sphinx . . . There she stands on the pavement, beckoning, so sternly to the red omnibus.

'How lovely! How well they play! How—how—how!'

The tongue is but a clapper. Simplicity itself. The feathers in the hat next to me are bright and pleasing as a child's rattle. The leaf on the plane-tree flashes green through the chink in the curtain. Very strange, very exciting.

'How—how—how!' Hush!

These are the lovers on the grass.

'If, madam, you will take my hand—'

'Sir, I would trust you with my heart. Moreover, we have left our bodies in the banqueting hall. Those on the turf are the shadows of our souls.'

'Then these are the embraces of our souls.' The lemons nod assent. The swan pushes from the bank and floats dreaming into mid stream.

'But to return. He followed me down the corridor, and, as we turned the corner, trod on the lace of my petticoat. What could I do but cry ("Ah!") and stop to finger it? At which he drew his sword, made passes as if he were stabbing something to death, and cried, "Mad! Mad! Mad!" Whereupon I screamed, and the Prince, who was writing in the large vellum book in the oriel window, came out in his velvet skull-cap and furred slippers, snatched a rapier from the wall—the King of Spain's gift, you know—on which I escaped, flinging on this cloak to hide the ravages to my skirt—to hide . . . But listen! the horns!'

The gentleman replies so fast to the lady, and she runs up the scale with such witty exchange of compliment now culminating in a sob of passion, that the words are indistinguishable though the meaning is plain enough—love, laughter, flight, pursuit, celestial bliss—all floated out on the gayest ripple of tender endearment—until the sound of the silver horns, at first far distant, gradually sounds more and more distinctly, as if seneschals were saluting the dawn or proclaiming ominously the escape of the lovers . . . The green garden, moonlit pool, lemons, lovers, and fish are all dissolved in the opal sky, across which, as the horns are joined by trumpets and supported by clarions there rise white arches firmly planted on marble pillars . . . Tramp and trumpeting. Clang and clangour. Firm establishment. Fast foundations. March of myriads. Confusion and chaos trod to earth. But this city to which we travel has neither stone nor marble; hangs enduring; stands unshakable; nor does a face, nor does a flag greet or welcome. Leave then to perish your hope; droop in the desert my joy; naked advance. Bare are the pillars; auspicious to none; casting no shade; resplendent; severe. Back then I fall, eager no more, desiring only to go, find the street, mark the buildings, greet the applewoman, say to the maid who opens the door: A starry night.

'Good night, good night. You go this way?'
'Alas. I go that.'

A SOCIETY

THIS is how it all came about. Six or seven of us were sitting one day after tea. Some were gazing across the street into the windows of a milliner's shop where the light still shone brightly upon scarlet feathers and golden slippers. Others were idly occupied in building little towers of sugar upon the edge of the tea tray. After a time, so far as I can remember, we drew round the fire and began as usual to praise men—how strong, how noble, how brilliant, how courageous, how beautiful they were—how we envied those who by hook or by crook managed to get attached to one for life—when Poll, who had said nothing, burst into tears. Poll, I must tell you, has always been queer. For one thing her father was a strange man. He left her a fortune in his will, but on condition that she read all the books in the London Library.* We comforted her as best we could; but we knew in our hearts how vain it was. For though we like her, Poll is no beauty; leaves her shoe laces untied; and must have been thinking, while we praised men, that not one of them would ever wish to marry her. At last she dried her tears. For some time we could make nothing of what she said. Strange enough it was in all conscience. She told us that, as we knew, she spent most of her time in the London Library, reading. She had begun, she said, with English literature on the top floor; and was steadily working her way down to *The Times* on the bottom. And now half, or perhaps only a quarter, way through a terrible thing had happened. She could read no more. Books were not what we thought them. 'Books' she cried, rising to her feet and speaking with an intensity of desolation which I shall never forget, 'are for the most part unutterably bad!'

Of course we cried out that Shakespeare wrote books, and Milton and Shelley.

'Oh yes,' she interrupted us. 'You've been well taught, I can see. But you are not members of the London Library.' Here her sobs broke forth anew. At length, recovering a little, she opened one of the pile of books which she always carried about with her—'From a Window' or 'In a Garden' or some such name as that it was called, and it was written by a man called Benton or Henson or something of that kind.* She read the first few pages. We listened in silence. 'But that's not a book,' someone said. So she chose another. This time it was a history, but I have forgotten the writer's name. Our trepidation increased as she went on. Not a word of it seemed to be true, and the style in which it was written was execrable.

'Poetry! Poetry!' we cried, impatiently. 'Read us poetry!' I cannot describe the desolation which fell upon us as she opened a little volume and mouthed out the verbose, sentimental foolery which it contained.

'It must have been written by a woman' one of us urged. But no. She told us that it was written by a young man, one of the most famous poets of the day. I leave you to imagine what the shock of the discovery was. Though we all cried and begged her to read no more she persisted and read us extracts from the Lives of the Lord Chancellors. When she had finished, Jane, the eldest and wisest of us, rose to her feet and said that she for one was not convinced.

'Why' she asked 'if men write such rubbish as this, should our mothers have wasted their youth in bringing them into the world?'

We were all silent; and in the silence, poor Poll could be heard sobbing out, 'Why, why did my father teach me to read?'

Clorinda was the first to come to her senses. 'It's all our fault' she said. 'Every one of us knows how to read. But no one, save Poll, has ever taken the trouble to do it. I, for one, have taken it for granted that it was a woman's duty to spend her youth in bearing children. I venerated my mother for bearing ten; still more my grandmother for bearing fifteen; it was, I confess, my own ambition to bear twenty. We have gone on all these ages supposing that men were equally industrious, and that their works were of equal merit. While we have borne the children, they, we supposed, have borne the books and the pictures. We have populated the world. They have civilized it. But now that we can read, what prevents us from judging the results? Before we bring another child into

the world we must swear that we will find out what the world is
like.'

So we made ourselves into a society for asking questions. One
of us was to visit a man-of-war; another was to hide herself in a
scholar's study; another was to attend a meeting of business men;
while all were to read books, look at pictures, go to concerts, keep
our eyes open in the streets; and ask questions perpetually. We
were very young. You can judge of our simplicity when I tell you
that before parting that night we agreed that the objects of life
were to produce good people and good books.* Our questions were
to be directed to finding out how far these objects were now
attained by men. We vowed solemnly that we would not bear a
single child until we were satisfied.

Off we went then, some to the British Museum; others to the
King's Navy; some to Oxford; others to Cambridge; we visited
the Royal Academy and the Tate; heard modern music in concert
rooms, went to the Law Courts, and saw new plays. No one dined
out without asking her partner certain questions and carefully
noting his replies. At intervals we met together and compared our
observations. Oh, those were merry meetings! Never have I
laughed so much as I did when Rose read her notes upon 'Honour' and described how she had dressed herself as an Ethiopian
Prince and gone aboard one of His Majesty's ships. Discovering
the hoax, the Captain visited her (now disguised as a private
gentleman) and demanded that honour should be satisfied. 'But
how?' she asked. 'How?' he bellowed. 'With the cane of course!'
Seeing that he was beside himself with rage and expecting that
her last moment had come, she bent over and received to her
amazement, six light taps upon the behind.* 'The honour of the
British Navy is avenged!' he cried, and, raising herself, she saw
him with the sweat pouring down his face holding out a trembling
right hand. 'Away!' she exclaimed, striking an attitude and imitating the ferocity of his own expression, 'My honour has still to be
satisfied!' 'Spoken like a gentleman!' he returned, and fell into
profound thought. 'If six strokes avenge the honour of the King's
Navy' he mused, 'how many avenge the honour of a private
gentleman?' He said he would prefer to lay the case before his

brother officers. She replied haughtily that she could not wait. He praised her sensibility. 'Let me see,' he cried suddenly, 'did your father keep a carriage?' 'No' she said. 'Or a riding horse?' 'We had a donkey,' she bethought her, 'which drew the mowing machine.' At this his face lightened. 'My mother's name—' she added. 'For God's sake, man, don't mention your mother's name!' he shrieked, trembling like an aspen and flushing to the roots of his hair, and it was ten minutes at least before she could induce him to proceed. At length he decreed that if she gave him four strokes and a half in the small of the back at a spot indicated by himself (the half conceded, he said, in recognition of the fact that her great grandmother's uncle was killed at Trafalgar*) it was his opinion that her honour would be as good as new. This was done; they retired to a restaurant; drank two bottles of wine for which he insisted upon paying; and parted with protestations of eternal friendship.

Then we had Fanny's account of her visit to the Law Courts.* At her first visit she had come to the conclusion that the Judges were either made of wood or were impersonated by large animals resembling man who had been trained to move with extreme dignity, mumble and nod their heads. To test her theory she had liberated a handkerchief of bluebottles at the critical moment of a trial, but was unable to judge whether the creatures gave signs of humanity for the buzzing of the flies induced so sound a sleep that she only woke in time to see the prisoners led into the cells below. But from the evidence she brought we voted that it is unfair to suppose that the Judges are men.

Helen went to the Royal Academy,* but when asked to deliver her report upon the pictures she began to recite from a pale blue volume 'O for the touch of a vanished hand and the sound of a voice that is still. Home is the hunter, home from the hill. He gave his bridle reins a shake. Love is sweet, love is brief. Spring, the fair spring, is the year's pleasant King. O! to be in England now that April's there. Men must work and women must weep. The path of duty is the way to glory—'* We could listen to no more of this gibberish.

'We want no more poetry!' we cried.

'Daughters of England!'* she began, but here we pulled her down, a vase of water getting spilt over her in the scuffle.

'Thank God!' she exclaimed, shaking herself like a dog. 'Now I'll roll on the carpet and see if I can't brush off what remains of the Union Jack. Then perhaps—' here she rolled energetically. Getting up she began to explain to us what modern pictures are like when Castalia* stopped her.

'What is the average size of a picture?' she asked. 'Perhaps two feet by two and a half,' she said. Castalia made notes while Helen spoke, and when she had done, and we were trying not to meet each others eyes, rose and said, 'At your wish I spent last week at Oxbridge, disguised as a charwoman. I thus had access to the rooms of several Professors and will now attempt to give you some idea—only,' she broke off, 'I can't think how to do it. It's all so queer. These Professors,' she went on, 'live in large houses built round grass plots each in a kind of cell by himself. Yet they have every convenience and comfort. You have only to press a button or light a little lamp. Their papers are beautifully filed. Books abound. There are no children or animals, save half a dozen stray cats and one aged bullfinch—a cock. I remember,' she broke off, 'an Aunt of mine who lived at Dulwich* and kept cactuses. You reached the conservatory through the double drawing-room, and there, on the hot pipes, were dozens of them, ugly, squat, bristly little plants each in a separate pot. Once in a hundred years the Aloe flowered,* so my Aunt said. But she died before that happened—' We told her to keep to the point. 'Well,' she resumed, 'when Professor Hobkin was out I examined his life work, an edition of Sappho.* It's a queer looking book, six or seven inches thick, not all by Sappho. Oh no. Most of it is a defence of Sappho's chastity, which some German had denied, and I can assure you the passion with which these two gentlemen argued, the learning they displayed, the prodigious ingenuity with which they disputed the use of some implement which looked to me for all the world like a hairpin astounded me; especially when the door opened and Professor Hobkin himself appeared. A very nice, mild, old gentleman, but what could *he* know about chastity?' We misunderstood her.

'No, no,' she protested, 'he's the soul of honour I'm sure—not that he resembles Rose's sea captain in the least. I was thinking rather of my Aunt's cactuses. What could *they* know about chastity?'

Again we told her not to wander from the point,—did the Oxbridge professors help to produce good people and good books?—the objects of life.

'There!' she exclaimed. 'It never struck me to ask. It never occurred to me that they could possibly produce anything.'

'I believe,' said Sue, 'that you made some mistake. Probably Professor Hobkin was a gynaecologist. A scholar is a very different sort of man. A scholar is overflowing with humour and invention—perhaps addicted to wine, but what of that?—a delightful companion, generous, subtle, imaginative—as stands to reason. For he spends his life in company with the finest human beings that have ever existed.'

'Hum,' said Castalia. 'Perhaps I'd better go back and try again.'

Some three months later it happened that I was sitting alone when Castalia entered. I don't know what it was in the look of her that so moved me; but I could not restrain myself, and dashing across the room, I clasped her in my arms. Not only was she very beautiful; she seemed also in the highest spirits. 'How happy you look!' I exclaimed, as she sat down.

'I've been at Oxbridge' she said.

'Asking questions?'

'Answering them' she replied.

'You have not broken our vow?' I said anxiously, noticing something about her figure.

'Oh, the vow' she said casually. 'I'm going to have a baby if that's what you mean. You can't imagine,' she burst out, 'how exciting, how beautiful, how satisfying—'

'What is?' I asked.

'To—to—answer questions,' she replied in some confusion. Whereupon she told me the whole of her story. But in the middle of an account which interested and excited me more than anything I had ever heard, she gave the strangest cry, half whoop, half holloa—

'Chastity! Chastity! Where's my chastity!' she cried. 'Help Ho! The scent bottle!'

There was nothing in the room but a cruet containing mustard, which I was about to administer when she recovered her composure.

'You should have thought of that three months ago' I said severely.

'True' she replied. 'There's not much good in thinking of it now. It was unfortunate, by the way, that my mother had me called Castalia.'

'Oh Castalia, your mother—' I was beginning when she reached for the mustard pot.

'No, no, no,' she said, shaking her head. 'If you'd been a chaste woman yourself you would have screamed at the sight of me—instead of which you rushed across the room and took me in your arms. No, Cassandra.* We are neither of us chaste.' So we went on talking.

Meanwhile the room was filling up, for it was the day appointed to discuss the results of our observations. Everyone, I thought, felt as I did about Castalia. They kissed her and said how glad they were to see her again. At length, when we were all assembled, Jane rose and said that it was time to begin. She began by saying that we had now asked questions for over five years, and that though the results were bound to be inconclusive—here Castalia nudged me and whispered that she was not so sure about that. Then she got up, and, interrupting Jane in the middle of a sentence, said,

'Before you say any more, I want to know—am I to stay in the room? Because,' she added 'I have to confess that I am an impure woman.'

Everyone looked at her in astonishment.

'You are going to have a baby?' asked Jane.

She nodded her head.

It was extraordinary to see the different expressions on their faces. A sort of hum went through the room, in which I could catch the words 'impure,' 'baby,' 'Castalia,' and so on. Jane, who was herself considerably moved, put it to us,

'Shall she go? Is she impure?'

Such a roar filled the room as might have been heard in the street outside.

'No! No! No! Let her stay! Impure? Fiddlesticks!' Yet I fancied that some of the youngest, girls of nineteen or twenty, held back as if overcome with shyness. Then we all came about her and began asking questions, and at last I saw one of the youngest, who had kept in the background, approach shyly and say to her:

'What is chastity then? I mean is it good, or is it bad, or is it nothing at all?' She replied so low that I could not catch what she said.

'You know I was shocked,' said another, 'for at least ten minutes.'

'In my opinion,' said Poll, who was growing crusty from always reading in the London Library, 'chastity is nothing but ignorance—a most discreditable state of mind. We should admit only the unchaste to our society. I vote that Castalia shall be our President.'

This was violently disputed.

'It is as unfair to brand women with chastity as with unchastity,' said Moll. 'Some of us haven't the opportunity either. Moreover, I don't believe Cassy herself maintains that she acted as she did from a pure love of knowledge.'

'He is only twenty one and divinely beautiful' said Cassy, with a ravishing gesture.

'I move,' said Helen, 'that no one be allowed to talk of chastity or unchastity save those who are in love.'

'Oh bother,' said Judith, who had been enquiring into scientific matters, 'I'm not in love and I'm longing to explain my measures for dispensing with prostitutes and fertilising virgins by Act of Parliament.'

She went on to tell us of an invention of hers to be erected at Tube stations and other public resorts, which, upon payment of a small fee would safeguard the nation's health, accommodate its sons, and relieve its daughters. Then she had contrived a method of preserving in sealed tubes the germs of future Lord Chancellors 'or poets or painters or musicians' she went on, 'supposing, that is to say, that these breeds are not extinct, and that women still wish to bear children—'*

'Of course we wish to bear children!' cried Castalia impatiently. Jane rapped the table.

'That is the very point we are met to consider,' she said. 'For five years we have been trying to find out whether we are justified in continuing the human race. Castalia has anticipated our decision. But it remains for the rest of us to make up our minds.'

Here one after another of our messengers rose and delivered their reports. The marvels of civilisation far exceeded our expectations, and as we learnt for the first time how man flies in the air, talks across space, penetrates to the heart of an atom, and embraces the universe in his speculations a murmur of admiration burst from our lips.

'We are proud,' we cried, 'that our mothers sacrificed their youth in such a cause as this!' Castalia, who had been listening intently, looked prouder than all the rest. Then Jane reminded us that we had still much to learn, and Castalia begged us to make haste. On we went through a vast tangle of statistics. We learnt that England has a population of so many millions, and that such and such a proportion of them is constantly hungry and in prison; that the average size of a working man's family is such, and that so great a percentage of women die from maladies incident to childbirth. Reports were read of visits to factories, shops, slums, and dockyards. Descriptions were given of the Stock Exchange, of a gigantic house of business in the City, and of a Government Office. The British Colonies were now discussed, and some account was given of our rule in India, Africa and Ireland. I was sitting by Castalia and I noticed her uneasiness.

'We shall never come to any conclusion at all at this rate,' she said. 'As it appears that civilisation is so much more complex than we had any notion, would it not be better to confine ourselves to our original enquiry? We agreed that it was the object of life to produce good people and good books. All this time we have been talking of aeroplanes, factories and money. Let us talk about men themselves and their arts, for that is the heart of the matter.'

So the diners out stepped forward with long slips of paper containing answers to their questions. These had been framed after much consideration. A good man, we had agreed, must at any rate be honest, passionate, and unworldly. But whether or not a particular man possessed those qualities could only be discovered by asking questions, often beginning at a remote distance from the centre. Is Kensington a nice place to live in? Where is your son being educated—and your daughter? Now please tell me, what do you pay for your cigars? By the way, is Sir Joseph a baronet or only a knight?* Often it seemed that we learnt more from trivial questions of this kind than from more direct ones. 'I accepted my peerage,' said Lord Bunkum 'because my wife wished it.' I forget how many titles were accepted for the same reason. 'Working fifteen hours out of the twenty-four as I do—' ten thousand professional men began.

'No, no, of course you can neither read nor write. But why do you work so hard?' 'My dear lady, with a growing family—' 'but *why* does your family grow?' Their wives wished that too, or perhaps it was the British Empire. But more significant than the answers were the refusals to answer. Very few would reply at all to questions about morality and religion, and such answers as were given were not serious. Questions as to the value of money and power were almost invariably brushed aside, or pressed at extreme risk to the asker. 'I'm sure,' said Jill, 'that if Sir Harley Tightboots hadn't been carving the mutton when I asked him about the capitalist system he would have cut my throat. The only reason why we escaped with our lives over and over again is that men are at once so hungry and so chivalrous. They despise us too much to mind what we say.'

'Of course they despise us' said Eleanor. 'At the same time how do you account for this—I made enquiries among the artists. Now no woman has ever been an artist, has she, Poll?'

'Jane-Austen-Charlotte-Bronte-George-Eliot,' cried Poll, like a man crying muffins in a back street.

'Damn the woman!' someone exclaimed. 'What a bore she is!'

'Since Sappho there has been no female of first rate—' Eleanor began, quoting from a weekly newspaper.

'It's now well known that Sappho was the somewhat lewd invention of Professor Hobkin,' Ruth interrupted.

'Anyhow, there is no reason to suppose that any woman ever has been able to write or ever will be able to write' Eleanor continued. 'And yet, whenever I go among authors they never cease to talk to me about their books. Masterly! I say, or Shakespeare himself! (for one must say something) and I assure you, they believe me.'

'That proves nothing,' said Jane. They all do it. 'Only,' she sighed, 'It doesn't seem to help *us* much. Perhaps we had better examine modern literature next. Liz, it's your turn.'

Elizabeth rose and said that in order to prosecute her enquiry she had dressed as a man and been taken for a reviewer.

'I have read new books pretty steadily for the past five years, said she.' 'Mr Wells is the most popular living writer; then comes Mr Arnold Bennett; then Mr Compton Mackenzie; Mr McKenna and Mr Walpole* may be bracketed together.' She sat down.

'But you've told us nothing!' we expostulated. 'Or do you mean that these gentlemen have greatly surpassed Jane-Eliot and that English fiction is—where's that review of yours? Oh, yes, "safe in their hands."'

'Safe, quite safe' she said, shifting uneasily from foot to foot. 'And I'm sure that they give away even more than they receive.'

We were all sure of that. 'But,' we pressed her, 'do they write good books?'

'Good books?' she said, looking at the ceiling. 'You must remember,' she began, speaking with extreme rapidity, 'that fiction is the mirror of life. And you can't deny that education is of the highest importance, and that it would be extremely annoying, if you found yourself alone at Brighton late at night, not to know which was the best boarding house to stay at, and suppose it was a dripping Sunday evening—wouldn't it be nice to go to the Movies?'

'But what has that got to do with it?' we asked.

'Nothing—nothing—nothing whatever' she replied.

'Well, tell us the truth' we bade her.

'The truth? But isn't it wonderful,' she broke off—'Mr Chitter has written a weekly article for the past thirty years upon love or hot buttered toast and has sent all his sons to Eton—'

'The truth!' we demanded.

'Oh the truth,' she stammered—'the truth has nothing to do with literature,' and sitting down she refused to say another word.

It all seemed to us very inconclusive.

'Ladies, we must try to sum up the results' Jane was beginning, when a hum, which had been heard for some time through the open window, drowned her voice.

'War! War! War! Declaration of War!'* men were shouting in the street below.

We looked at each other in horror.

'What war?' we cried. 'What war?' We remembered, too late, that we had never thought of sending anyone to the House of Commons. We had forgotten all about it. We turned to Poll, who had reached the history shelves in the London Library, and asked her to enlighten us.

'Why,' we cried 'do men go to war?'

'Sometimes for one reason, sometimes for another' she replied calmly. 'In 1760, for example—' The shouts outside drowned her words. 'Again in 1797—in 1804—It was the Austrians in 1866—1870 was the Franco-Prussian—In 1900 on the other hand—'*

'But it's now 1914!' we cut her short.

'Ah, I don't know what they're going to war for now,' she admitted.

*

The war was over and peace was in process of being signed when I once more found myself with Castalia in the room where our meetings used to be held. We began idly turning over the pages of our old minute books. 'Queer,' I mused, 'to see what we were thinking five years ago.' 'We are agreed,' Castalia quoted, reading over my shoulder, 'that it is the object to life to produce good people and good books.' We made no comment upon that. 'A good man is at any rate honest passionate and unworldly.' 'What a woman's language' I observed. 'Oh dear,' cried Castalia, pushing the book away from her, 'What fools we were! It was all Poll's father's fault,' she went on. 'I believe he did it on purpose—that ridiculous will, I mean, forcing Poll to read all the books in the London Library. If we hadn't learnt to read,' she said bitterly, 'we might still have been bearing children in ignorance and that I believe was the happiest life after all. I know what you're going to say about war,' she checked me, 'and the horror of bearing children to see them killed, but our mothers did it, and their mothers, and their mothers before them. And *they* didn't complain. They couldn't read. I've done my best,' she sighed, 'to prevent my little girl from learning to read, but what's the use? I caught Ann only yesterday with a newspaper in her hand and she was beginning to ask me if it was "true". Next she'll ask me whether Mr Lloyd George* is a good man, then whether Mr Arnold Bennett is a good novelist, and finally whether I believe in God. How can I bring my daughter up to believe in nothing?' she demanded.

'Surely you could teach her to believe that a man's intellect is, and always will be, fundamentally superior to a woman's?' I suggested. She brightened at this and began to turn over our old minutes again. 'Yes,' she said, 'think of their discoveries, their mathematics, their science, their philosophy, their scholarship—' and then she began to laugh, 'I shall never forget old Hobkin and the hairpin,' she said, and went on reading and laughing and I thought she was quite happy, when suddenly she threw the book from her and burst out, 'Oh, Cassandra why do you torment me? Don't you know that our belief in man's intellect is the greatest fallacy of them all?' 'What?' I exclaimed. 'Ask any journalist, schoolmaster, politician or public house keeper in the land and they will all tell you that men are much cleverer than women.' 'As if I doubted it,' she said scornfully. 'How could they help it? Haven't we bred them and fed and kept them in comfort since the beginning of time so that they may be clever even if they're nothing else? It's all our doing!' she cried. 'We insisted upon having intellect and now we've got it. And it's intellect,' she continued, 'that's at the bottom of it. What could be more charming than a boy before he has begun to cultivate his intellect? He is beautiful to look at; he gives himself no airs; he understands the meaning of art and literature instinctively; he goes about enjoying his life and making other people enjoy theirs. Then they teach him to cultivate his intellect. He becomes a barrister, a civil servant, a general, an author, a professor. Every day he goes to an office. Every year he produces a book. He maintains a whole family by the products of his brain—poor devil! Soon he cannot come into a room without making us all feel uncomfortable; he condescends to every woman he meets, and dares not tell the truth even to his own wife; instead of rejoicing our eyes we have to shut them if we are to take him in our arms. True, they console themselves with stars of all shapes, ribbons of all shades, and incomes of all sizes—but what is to console us? That we shall be able in ten years' time to spend a weekend at Lahore?* Or that the least insect in Japan has a name twice the length of its body? Oh, Cassandra, for Heaven's sake let us devise a method by which men may bear children! It is our only chance. For unless we provide them with some innocent occupation we shall get neither good people nor good books; we shall perish beneath the fruits of their unbridled activity; and not a human being will survive to know that there once was Shakespeare!'

'It is too late,' I said. 'We cannot provide even for the children that we have.'

'And then you ask me to believe in intellect,' she said.

While we spoke, men were crying hoarsely and wearily in the street, and listening, we heard that the Treaty of Peace had just been signed.* The voices died away. The rain was falling and interfered no doubt with the proper explosion of the fireworks.

'My cook will have bought the *Evening News*' said Castalia 'and Ann will be spelling it out over her tea. I must go home.'

'It's no good—not a bit of good' I said. 'Once she knows how to read there's only one thing you can teach her to believe in—and that is herself.'

'Well, that would be a change,' said Castalia.

So we swept up the papers of our Society, and though Ann was playing with her doll very happily, we solemnly made her a present of the lot and told her we had chosen her to be President of the Society of the future—upon which she burst into tears, poor little girl.

SOLID OBJECTS

THE only thing that moved upon the vast semi-circle of the beach
was one small black spot. As it came nearer to the ribs and spine
of the stranded pilchard boat, it became apparent from a certain
tenuity in its blackness that this spot possessed four legs; and
moment by moment it became more unmistakable that it was
composed of the persons of two young men. Even thus in outline
against the sand there was an unmistakable vitality in them; an
indescribable vigour in the approach and withdrawal of the bodies, slight though it was, which proclaimed some violent argument issuing from the tiny mouths of the little round heads. This
was corroborated on closer view by the repeated lunging of a
walking-stick on the right-hand side. 'You mean to tell me . . .
You actually believe . . . ' thus the walking-stick on the right-
hand side next the waves seemed to be asserting as it cut long
straight stripes upon the sand.

'Politics be damned!'* issued clearly from the body on the left-
hand side, and, as these words were uttered, the mouths, noses,
chins, little moustaches, tweed caps, rough boots, shooting coats,
and check stockings of the two speakers became clearer and
clearer; the smoke of their pipes went up into the air; nothing was
so solid, so living, so hard, red, hirsute and virile as these two
bodies for miles and miles of sea and sandhill.

They flung themselves down by the six ribs and spine of the
black pilchard boat. You know how the body seems to shake itself
free from an argument, and to apologize for a mood of exaltation;
flinging itself down and expressing in the looseness of its attitude
a readiness to take up with something new—whatever it may be
that comes next to hand. So Charles, whose stick had been slash-
ing the beach for half a mile or so, began skimming flat pieces of
slate over the water; and John, who had exclaimed 'Politics be
damned!' began burrowing his fingers down, down, into the sand.
As his hand went further and further beyond the wrist, so that he
had to hitch his sleeve a little higher, his eyes lost their intensity,

or rather the background of thought and experience which gives an inscrutable depth to the eyes of grown people disappeared, leaving only the clear transparent surface, expressing nothing but wonder, which the eyes of young children display. No doubt the act of burrowing in the sand had something to do with it. He remembered that, after digging for a little, the water oozes round your finger-tips; the hole then becomes a moat; a well; a spring; a secret channel to the sea. As he was choosing which of these things to make it, still working his fingers in the water, they curled round something hard—a full drop of solid matter—and gradually dislodged a large irregular lump, and brought it to the surface. When the sand coating was wiped off, a green tint appeared. It was a lump of glass, so thick as to be almost opaque; the smoothing of the sea had completely worn off any edge or shape, so that it was impossible to say whether it had been bottle, tumbler or window-pane; it was nothing but glass; it was almost a precious stone. You had only to enclose it in a rim of gold, or pierce it with a wire, and it became a jewel; part of a necklace, or a dull, green light upon a finger. Perhaps after all it was really a gem; something worn by a dark Princess trailing her finger in the water as she sat in the stern of the boat and listened to the slaves singing as they rowed her across the Bay. Or the oak sides of a sunk Elizabethan treasure-chest had split apart, and, rolled over and over, over and over, its emeralds had come at last to shore. John turned it in his hands; he held it to the light; he held it so that its irregular mass blotted out the body and extended right arm of his friend. The green thinned and thickened slightly as it was held against the sky or against the body. It pleased him; it puzzled him; it was so hard, so concentrated, so definite an object compared with the vague sea and the hazy shore.

Now a sigh disturbed him—profound, final, making him aware that his friend Charles had thrown all the flat stones within reach, or had come to the conclusion that it was not worth while to throw them. They ate their sandwiches side by side. When they had done, and were shaking themselves and rising to their feet, John took the lump of glass and looked at it in silence. Charles looked at it too. But he saw immediately that it was not flat, and filling his pipe he said with the energy that dismisses a foolish strain of thought,

'To return to what I was saying—'

He did not see, or if he had seen would hardly have noticed, that John after looking at the lump for a moment, as if in hesitation, slipped it inside his pocket. That impulse, too, may have been the impulse which leads a child to pick up one pebble on a path strewn with them, promising it a life of warmth and security upon the nursery mantelpiece, delighting in the sense of power and benignity which such an action confers, and believing that the heart of the stone leaps with joy when it sees itself chosen from a million like it, to enjoy this bliss instead of a life of cold and wet upon the high road. 'It might so easily have been any other of the millions of stones, but it was I, I, I!'

Whether this thought or not was in John's mind: the lump of glass had its place upon the mantelpiece, where it stood heavy upon a little pile of bills and letters, and served not only as an excellent paperweight, but also as a natural stopping place for the young man's eyes when they wandered from his book. Looked at again and again half consciously by a mind thinking of something else, any object mixes itself so profoundly with the stuff of thought that it loses its actual form and recomposes itself a little differently in an ideal shape which haunts the brain when we least expect it. So John found himself attracted to the windows of curiosity shops when he was out walking, merely because he saw something which reminded him of the lump of glass. Anything, so long as it was an object of some kind, more or less round, perhaps with a dying flame deep sunk in its mass, anything—china, glass, amber, rock, marble—even the smooth oval egg of a prehistoric bird would do. He took, also, to keeping his eyes upon the ground, especially in the neighbourhood of waste land where the household refuse is thrown away. Such objects often occurred there—thrown away, of no use to anybody, shapeless, discarded. In a few months he had collected four or five specimens that took their place upon the mantelpiece. They were useful, too, for a man who is standing for Parliament upon the brink of a brilliant career has any number of papers to keep in order—addresses to constituents, declarations of policy, appeals for subscriptions, invitations to dinner, and so on.

One day, starting from his rooms in the Temple* to catch a train in order to address his constituents, his eyes rested upon a remarkable object lying half-hidden in one of those little borders of grass which edge the bases of vast legal buildings. He could only touch it with the point of his stick through the railings; but he could see that it was a piece of china of the most remarkable shape, as nearly resembling a starfish as anything—shaped, or broken accidentally, into five irregular but unmistakable points. The colouring was mainly blue, but green stripes or spots of some kind overlaid the blue, and lines of crimson gave it a richness and lustre of the most attractive kind. John was determined to possess it; but the more he pushed, the further it receded. At length he was forced to go back to his rooms and improvise a wire ring attached to the end of a stick, with which, by dint of great care and skill, he finally drew the piece of china within reach of his hands. As he seized hold of it he exclaimed in triumph. At that moment the clock struck. It was out of the question that he should keep his appointment. The meeting was held without him. But how had the piece of china been broken into this remarkable shape? A careful examination put it beyond doubt that the star shape was accidental, which made it all the more strange, and it seemed unlikely that there should be another such in existence. Set at the opposite end of the mantelpiece from the lump of glass that had been dug from the sand, it looked like a creature from another world—freakish and fantastic as a harlequin. It seemed to be pirouetting through space; winking light like a fitful star. The contrast between the china so vivid and alert, and the glass so mute and contemplative, fascinated him, and wondering and amazed he asked himself how the two came to exist in the same world, let alone to stand upon the same narrow strip of marble in the same room. The question remained unanswered.

He now began to haunt the places which are most prolific of broken china, such as pieces of waste land between railway lines, sites of demolished houses, and commons in the neighbourhood of London. But china is seldom thrown from a great height; it is one of the rarest of human actions. You have to find in conjunction a very high house, and a woman of such reckless impulse and passionate prejudice that she flings her jar or pot straight from the window without thought of who is below. Broken china was to be found in plenty, but broken in some trifling domestic accident, without purpose or character. Nevertheless, he was often astonished, as he came to go into the question more deeply, by the immense variety of shapes to be found in London alone, and there was still more cause for wonder and speculation in the differences of qualities and designs. The finest specimens he would bring home and place upon his mantelpiece, where, however, their duty was more and more of an ornamental nature, since papers needing a weight to keep them down became scarcer and scarcer.

He neglected his duties, perhaps, or discharged them absent-mindedly, or his constituents when they visited him were unfavourably impressed by the appearance of his mantelpiece. At any rate he was not elected to represent them in Parliament, and his friend Charles, taking it much to heart and hurrying to condole with him, found him so little cast down by the disaster that he could only suppose that it was too serious a matter for him to realize all at once.

In truth, John had been that day to Barnes Common,* and there under a furse bush had found a very remarkable piece of iron. It was almost identical with the glass in shape, massy and globular, but so cold and heavy, so black and metallic, that it was evidently alien to the earth and had its origin in one of the dead stars or was itself the cinder of a moon. It weighed his pocket down; it weighed the mantelpiece down; it radiated cold. And yet the meteorite stood upon the same ledge with the lump of glass and the star-shaped china.

As his eyes passed from one to another, the determination to possess objects that even surpassed these tormented the young man. He devoted himself more and more resolutely to the search. If he had not been consumed by ambition and convinced that one day some newly-discovered rubbish heap would reward him, the disappointments he had suffered, let alone the fatigue and derision, would have made him give up the pursuit. Provided with a bag and a long stick fitted with an adaptable hook, he ransacked all deposits of earth; raked beneath matted tangles of scrub; searched all alleys and spaces between walls where he had learned to expect to find objects of this kind thrown away. As his standard became higher and his taste more severe the disappointments were innumerable, but always some gleam of hope, some piece of china or glass curiously marked or broken, lured him on. Day after day passed. He was no longer young. His career—that is, his political career—was a thing of the past. People gave up visiting him. He was too silent to be worth asking to dinner. He never talked to anyone about his serious ambitions; their lack of understanding was apparent in their behaviour.

He leaned back in his chair now and watched Charles lift the stones on the mantelpiece a dozen times and put them down emphatically to mark what he was saying about the conduct of the Government, without once noticing their existence.

'What was the truth of it, John?' asked Charles suddenly, turning and facing him. 'What made you give it up like that all in a second?'

'I've not given it up,' John replied.

'But you've not the ghost of a chance now,' said Charles roughly.

'I don't agree with you there,' said John with conviction. Charles looked at him and was profoundly uneasy; the most extraordinary doubts possessed him; he had a queer sense that they were talking about different things. He looked round to find some relief for his horrible depression, but the disorderly appearance of the room depressed him still further. What was that stick, and the old carpet bag hanging against the wall? And then those stones? Looking at John, something fixed and distant in his expression alarmed him. He knew only too well that his mere appearance upon a platform was out of the question.

'Pretty stones,' he said as cheerfully as he could; and saying that he had an appointment to keep, he left John—for ever.

IN THE ORCHARD

MIRANDA slept in the orchard, lying in a long chair beneath the apple tree. Her book had fallen into the grass, and her finger still seemed to point at the sentence '*Ce pays est vraiment un des coins du monde où le rire des filles éclate le mieux . . .* '* as if she had fallen asleep just there. The opals on her finger flushed green, flushed rosy, and again flushed orange as the sun, oozing through the apple trees, filled them. Then, when the breeze blew, her purple dress rippled like a flower attached to a stalk; the grasses nodded; and the white butterfly came blowing this way and that just above her face.

Four feet in the air over her head the apples hung. Suddenly there was a shrill clamour as if they were gongs of cracked brass beaten violently, irregularly, and brutally. It was only the schoolchildren saying the multiplication table in unison, stopped by the teacher, scolded, and beginning to say the multiplication table over again. But this clamour passed four feet above Miranda's head, went through the apple boughs, and, striking against the cowman's little boy who was picking blackberries in the hedge when he should have been at school, made him tear his thumb on the thorns.

Next there was a solitary cry—sad, human, brutal. Old Parsley was, indeed, blind drunk.

Then the very topmost leaves of the apple tree, flat like little fish against the blue, thirty feet above the earth, chimed with a pensive and lugubrious note. It was the organ in the church playing one of Hymns Ancient and Modern.* The sound floated out and was cut into atoms by a flock of fieldfares flying at an enormous speed—somewhere or other. Miranda lay asleep thirty feet beneath.

Then above the apple tree and the pear tree two hundred feet above Miranda lying asleep in the orchard bells thudded, intermittent, sullen, didactic, for six poor women of the parish were being churched and the Rector was returning thanks to heaven.

And above that with a sharp squeak the golden feather of the church tower* turned from south to east. The wind changed. Above everything else it droned, above the woods, the meadows, the hills, miles above Miranda lying in the orchard asleep. It swept on, eyeless, brainless, meeting nothing that could stand against it, until, wheeling the other way, it turned south again. Miles below, in a space as big as the eye of a needle, Miranda stood upright and cried aloud: 'Oh, I shall be late for tea!'

Miranda slept in the orchard—or perhaps she was not asleep, for her lips moved very slightly as if they were saying, '*Ce pays est vraiment un des coins du monde . . . où le rire des filles . . . éclate . . . éclate . . . éclate . . .* ' and then she smiled and let her body sink all its weight on to the enormous earth which rises, she thought, to carry me on its back as if I were a leaf, or a queen (here the children said the multiplication table), or, Miranda went on, I might be lying on the top of a cliff with the gulls screaming above me. The higher they fly, she continued, as the teacher scolded the children and rapped Jimmy over the knuckles till they bled, the deeper they look into the sea—into the sea, she repeated, and her fingers relaxed and her lips closed gently as if she were floating on the sea, and then, when the shout of the drunken man sounded overhead, she drew breath with an extraordinary ecstasy, for she thought that she heard life itself crying out from a rough tongue in a scarlet mouth, from the wind, from the bells, from the curved green leaves of the cabbages.

Naturally she was being married when the organ played the tune from Hymns Ancient and Modern, and, when the bells rang after the six poor women had been churched, the sullen intermittent thud made her think that the very earth shook with the hoofs of the horse that was galloping towards her ('Ah, I have only to wait!' she sighed), and it seemed to her that everything had already begun moving, crying, riding, flying round her, across her, towards her in a pattern.

Mary is chopping the wood, she thought; Pearman is herding the cows; the carts are coming up from the meadows; the rider— and she traced out the lines that the men, the carts, the birds, and the rider made over the countryside until they all seemed driven out, round, and across by the beat of her own heart.

Miles up in the air the wind changed; the golden feather of the church tower squeaked; and Miranda jumped up and cried: 'Oh, I shall be late for tea!'

Miranda slept in the orchard, or was she asleep or was she not asleep? Her purple dress stretched between the two apple trees. There were twenty-four apple trees in the orchard, some slanting slightly, others growing straight with a rush up the trunk which spread wide into branches and formed into round red or yellow drops. Each apple tree had sufficient space. The sky exactly fitted the leaves. When the breeze blew, the line of the boughs against the wall slanted slightly and then returned. A wagtail flew diagonally from one corner to another. Cautiously hopping, a thrush advanced towards a fallen apple; from the other wall a sparrow fluttered just above the grass. The uprush of the trees was tied down by these movements; the whole was compacted by the orchard walls. For miles beneath the earth was clamped together; rippled on the surface with wavering air; and across the corner of the orchard the blue-green was slit by a purple streak. The wind changing, one bunch of apples was tossed so high that it blotted out two cows in the meadow ('Oh, I shall be late for tea!' cried Miranda), and the apples hung straight across the wall again.

THE LADY IN THE LOOKING-GLASS:
A REFLECTION

PEOPLE should not leave looking-glasses hanging in their rooms any more than they should leave open cheque books or letters confessing some hideous crime. One could not help looking, that summer afternoon, in the long glass that hung outside in the hall. Chance had so arranged it. From the depths of the sofa in the drawing-room one could see reflected in the Italian glass not only the marble-topped table opposite, but a stretch of the garden beyond. One could see a long grass path leading between banks of tall flowers until, slicing off an angle, the gold rim cut it off.

The house was empty, and one felt, since one was the only person in the drawing-room, like one of those naturalists who, covered with grass and leaves, lie watching the shyest animals— badgers, otters, kingfishers—moving about freely, themselves unseen. The room that afternoon was full of such shy creatures, lights and shadows, curtains blowing, petals falling—things that never happen, so it seems, if someone is looking. The quiet old country room with its rugs and stone chimney pieces, its sunken book-cases and red and gold lacquer cabinets, was full of such nocturnal creatures. They came pirouetting across the floor, stepping delicately with high-lifted feet and spread tails and peck- ing allusive beaks as if they had been cranes or flocks of elegant flamingoes whose pink was faded, or peacocks whose trains were veined with silver. And there were obscure flushes and darken- ings too, as if a cuttlefish had suddenly suffused the air with purple; and the room had its passions and rages and envies and sorrows coming over it and clouding it, like a human being. Nothing stayed the same for two seconds together.

But, outside, the looking-glass reflected the hall table, the sun- flowers, the garden path so accurately and so fixedly that they seemed held there in their reality unescapably. It was a strange contrast—all changing here, all stillness there. One could not help looking from one to the other. Meanwhile, since all the doors and windows were open in the heat, there was a perpetual sighing and ceasing sound, the voice of the transient and the perishing, it seemed, coming and going like human breath, while in the looking-glass things had ceased to breathe and lay still in the trance of immortality.

Half an hour ago the mistress of the house, Isabella Tyson, had gone down the grass path in her thin summer dress, carrying a basket, and had vanished, sliced off by the gilt rim of the looking-glass. She had gone presumably into the lower garden to pick flowers; or as it seemed more natural to suppose, to pick something light and fantastic and leafy and trailing, traveller's joy, or one of those elegant sprays of convolvulus that twine round ugly walls and burst here and there into white and violet blossoms. She suggested the fantastic and the tremulous convolvulus rather than the upright aster, the starched zinnia, or her own burning roses alight like lamps on the straight posts of their rose trees. The comparison showed how very little, after all these years, one knew about her; for it is impossible that any woman of flesh and blood of fifty-five or sixty should be really a wreath or a tendril. Such comparisons are worse than idle and superficial—they are cruel even, for they come like the convolvulus itself trembling between one's eyes and the truth. There must be truth; there must be a wall. Yet it was strange that after knowing her all these years one could not say what the truth about Isabella was; one still made up phrases like this about convolvulus and traveller's joy. As for facts, it was a fact that she was a spinster; that she was rich; that she had bought this house and collected with her own hands— often in the most obscure corners of the world and at great risk from poisonous stings and Oriental diseases—the rugs, the chairs, the cabinets which now lived their nocturnal life before one's eyes. Sometimes it seemed as if they knew more about her than we, who sat on them, wrote at them, and trod on them so carefully, were allowed to know. In each of these cabinets were many little drawers, and each almost certainly held letters, tied with bows of ribbon, sprinkled with sticks of lavender or rose leaves. For it was another fact—if facts were what one wanted— that Isabella had known many people, had had many friends; and thus if one had the audacity to open a drawer and read her letters, one would find the traces of many agitations, of appointments to meet, of upbraidings for not having met, long letters of intimacy and affection, violent letters of jealousy and reproach, terrible final words of parting—for all those interviews and assignations had led to nothing—that is, she had never married, and yet, judging from the mask-like indifference of her face, she had gone through twenty times more of passion and experience than those whose loves are trumpeted forth for all the world to hear. Under the stress of thinking about Isabella, her room became more shadowy and symbolic; the corners seemed darker, the legs of chairs and tables more spindly and hieroglyphic.

Suddenly these reflections were ended violently and yet without a sound. A large black form loomed into the looking-glass; blotted out everything, strewed the table with a packet of marble tablets veined with pink and grey, and was gone. But the picture was entirely altered. For the moment it was unrecognisable and irrational and entirely out of focus. One could not relate these tablets to any human purpose. And then by degrees some logical process set to work on them and began ordering and arranging them and bringing them into the fold of common experience. One realised at last that they were merely letters. The man had brought the post.

There they lay on the marble-topped table, all dripping with light and colour at first and crude and unabsorbed. And then it was strange to see how they were drawn in and arranged and composed and made part of the picture and granted that stillness and immortality which the looking-glass conferred. They lay there invested with a new reality and significance and with a greater heaviness, too, as if it would have needed a chisel to dislodge them from the table. And, whether it was fancy or not, they seemed to have become not merely a handful of casual letters but to be tablets graven with eternal truth—if one could read them, one would know everything there was to be known about Isabella, yes, and about life, too. The pages inside those marble-looking envelopes must be cut deep and scored thick with meaning. Isabella would come in, and take them, one by one, very slowly, and open them, and read them carefully word by word, and then with a profound sigh of comprehension, as if she had seen to the bottom of everything, she would tear the envelopes to little bits and tie the letters together and lock the cabinet drawer in her determination to conceal what she did not wish to be known.

The thought served as a challenge. Isabella did not wish to be known—but she should no longer escape. It was absurd, it was monstrous. If she concealed so much and knew so much one must prize her open with the first tool that came to hand—the imagination. One must fix one's mind upon her at that very moment. One must fasten her down there. One must refuse to be put off any longer with sayings and doings such as the moment brought forth—with dinners and visits and polite conversations. One must put oneself in her shoes. If one took the phrase literally, it was easy to see the shoes in which she stood, down in the lower garden, at this moment. They were very narrow and long and fashionable—they were made of the softest and most flexible leather. Like everything she wore, they were exquisite. And she would be standing under the high hedge in the lower part of the garden, raising the scissors that were tied to her waist to cut some dead flower, some overgrown branch. The sun would beat down on her face, into her eyes; but no, at the critical moment a veil of cloud covered the sun, making the expression of her eyes doubtful—was it mocking or tender, brilliant or dull? One could only see the indeterminate outline of her rather faded, fine face looking at the sky. She was thinking, perhaps, that she must order a new net for the strawberries; that she must send flowers to Johnson's widow; that it was time she drove over to see the Hippesleys in their new house. Those were the things she talked about at dinner certainly. But one was tired of the things that she talked about at dinner. It was her profounder state of being that one wanted to catch and turn to words, the state that is to the mind what breathing is to the body, what one calls happiness or unhappiness. At the mention of those words it became obvious, surely, that she must be happy. She was rich; she was distinguished; she had many friends; she travelled—she bought rugs in Turkey and blue pots in Persia. Avenues of pleasure radiated this way and that from where she stood with her scissors raised to cut the trembling branches while the lacy clouds veiled her face.

Here with a quick movement of her scissors she snipped the spray of traveller's joy and it fell to the ground. As it fell, surely some light came in too, surely one could penetrate a little farther into her being. Her mind then was filled with tenderness and regret . . . To cut an overgrown branch saddened her because it had once lived, and life was dear to her. Yes, and at the same time the fall of the branch would suggest to her how she must die herself and all the futility and evanescence of things. And then again quickly catching this thought up, with her instant good sense, she thought life had treated her well; even if fall she must, it was to lie on the earth and moulder sweetly into the roots of violets. So she stood thinking. Without making any thought precise—for she was one of those reticent people whose minds hold their thoughts enmeshed in clouds of silence—she was filled with thoughts. Her mind was like her room, in which lights advanced and retreated, came pirouetting and stepping delicately, spread their tails, pecked their way; and then her whole being was suffused, like the room again, with a cloud of some profound knowledge, some unspoken regret, and then she was full of locked drawers, stuffed with letters, like her cabinets. To talk of 'prizing her open' as if she were an oyster, to use any but the finest and subtlest and most pliable tools upon her was impious and absurd. One must imagine—here was she in the looking-glass. It made one start.

She was so far off at first that one could not see her clearly. She came lingering and pausing, here straightening a rose, there lifting a pink to smell it, but she never stopped; and all the time she became larger and larger in the looking-glass, more and more completely the person into whose mind one had been trying to penetrate. One verified her by degrees—fitted the qualities one had discovered into this visible body. There were her grey-green dress, and her long shoes, her basket, and something sparkling at her throat. She came so gradually that she did not seem to derange the pattern in the glass, but only to bring in some new element which gently moved and altered the other objects as if asking them, courteously, to make room for her. And the letters and the table and the grass walk and the sunflowers which had been waiting in the looking-glass separated and opened out so that she might be received among them. At last there she was, in the hall. She stopped dead. She stood by the table. She stood perfectly still. At once the looking-glass began to pour over her a light that seemed to fix her; that seemed like some acid to bite off the unessential and superficial and to leave only the truth. It was an enthralling spectacle. Everything dropped from her—clouds, dress, basket, diamond—all that one had called the creeper and convolvulus. Here was the hard wall beneath. Here was the woman herself. She stood naked in that pitiless light. And there was nothing. Isabella was perfectly empty. She had no thoughts. She had no friends. She cared for nobody. As for her letters, they were all bills. Look, as she stood there, old and angular, veined and lined, with her high nose and her wrinkled neck, she did not even trouble to open them.

People should not leave looking-glasses hanging in their rooms.

THE SHOOTING PARTY

SHE got in and put her suitcase on the rack, and the brace of pheasants on top of it. Then she sat down in the corner. The train was rattling through the Midlands, and the fog, which came in when she opened the door, seemed to enlarge the carriage and set the four travellers apart. Obviously M. M.—those were the initials on the suitcase—had been staying the weekend with a shooting party—obviously, for she was telling over the story now, lying back in her corner. She did not shut her eyes. But clearly she did not see the man opposite, nor the coloured photograph of York Minster.* She must have heard, too, what they had been saying. For as she gazed, her lips moved; now and then she smiled. And she was handsome; a cabbage rose; a russet apple; tawny; but scarred on the jaw—the scar lengthened when she smiled. Since she was telling over the story she must have been a guest there, and yet, dressed as she was, out of fashion, as women dressed, years ago, in pictures in fashion plates of sporting newspapers, she did not seem exactly a guest, nor yet a maid. Had she had a basket with her she would have been the woman who breeds fox-terriers; the owner of the Siamese cat; someone connected with hounds and horses. But she had only a suitcase and the pheasants. Somehow, therefore, she must have wormed her way into the room that she was seeing through the stuffing of the carriage, and the man's bald head, and the picture of York Minster. And she must have listened to what they were saying, for now, like somebody imitating the noise that someone else makes, she made a little click at the back of her throat: 'Chk,' 'Chk.'* Then she smiled.

'Chk' said Miss Antonia, pinching her glasses on her nose. The damp leaves fell across the long windows of the gallery; one or two stuck, fish-shaped, and lay like inlaid brown wood upon the window-panes. Then the trees in the Park shivered, and the leaves, flaunting down, seemed to make the shiver visible—the damp brown shiver.

'Chk' Miss Antonia sniffed again, and pecked at the flimsy white stuff that she held in her hands, as a hen pecks nervously, rapidly at a piece of white bread.

The wind sighed. The room was draughty. The doors did not fit, nor the windows. Now and then a ripple, like a reptile, ran under the carpet. On the carpet lay panels of green and yellow, where the sun rested, and then the sun moved and pointed a finger as if in mockery at a hole in the carpet and stopped. And then on it went, the sun's feeble but impartial finger, and lay upon the coat of arms over the fireplace; gently illumined the shield; the pendant grapes; the mermaid; and the spears.* Miss Antonia looked up as the light strengthened. Vast lands, so they said, the old people had owned—her forefathers—the Rashleighs. Over there. Up the Amazons. Freebooters. Voyagers. Sacks of emeralds. Nosing round the islands. Taking captives. Maidens. There she was, all scales from the tail to the waist. Miss Antonia grinned. Down struck the finger of the sun and her eye went with it. Now it rested on a silver frame; on a photograph; on an egg-shaped baldish head; on a lip that stuck out under the moustache; and the name 'Edward' written with a flourish beneath.*

'The King . . . ' Miss Antonia muttered, turning the film of white upon her knee, 'had the Blue Room,' she added with a toss of her head. The light faded.

Out in the King's Ride the pheasants were being driven across the noses of the guns. Up they spurted from the underwood like heavy rockets, reddish-purple rockets, and as they rose the guns cracked in order, eagerly, sharply, as if a line of dogs had suddenly barked. Tufts of white smoke held together for a moment; then gently solved themselves, faded, and dispersed.

In the deep-cut road beneath the hanger a cart stood, laid already with soft warm bodies, with limp claws and still lustrous eyes. The birds seemed alive still, but swooning under their rich damp feathers. They looked relaxed and comfortable, stirring slightly, as if they slept upon a warm bank of soft feathers on the floor of the cart.

Then the Squire, with the hang-dog, purple-stained face, in the shabby gaiters, cursed and raised his gun.

Miss Antonia stitched on. Now and then a tongue of flame reached round the grey log that stretched from one bar to another across the grate; ate it greedily, then died out, leaving a white bracelet where the bark had been eaten off. Miss Antonia looked up for a moment, stared wide-eyed, instinctively, as a dog stares at a flame. Then the flame sank and she stitched again.

Then, silently, the enormously high door opened. Two lean men came in, and drew a table over the hole in the carpet. They went out; they came in. They laid a cloth upon the table. They went out: they came in. They brought a green baize basket of knives and forks; and glasses; and sugar casters; and salt-cellars; and bread; and a silver vase with three chrysanthemums in it. And the table was laid. Miss Antonia stitched on.

Again the door opened, pushed feebly this time. A little dog trotted in, a spaniel, nosing nimbly; it paused. The door stood open. And then, leaning on her stick, heavily, old Miss Rashleigh* entered. A white shawl, diamond fastened, clouded her baldness. She hobbled; crossed the room; hunched herself in the high-backed chair by the fireside. Miss Antonia went on stitching.

'Shooting,' she said at last.

Old Miss Rashleigh nodded. 'In the King's Ride,' she said. She gripped her stick. They sat waiting.

The shooters had moved now from the King's Ride to the Home Woods. They stood in the purple ploughed field outside. Now and then a twig snapped; leaves came whirling. But above the mist and the smoke was an island of blue—faint blue, pure blue— alone in the sky. And in the innocent air, as if straying alone like a cherub, a bell from a far hidden steeple frolicked, gambolled, then faded. Then again up shot the rockets, the reddish-purple pheasants. Up and up they went. Again the guns barked; the smoke balls formed; loosened, dispersed. And the busy little dogs ran nosing nimbly over the fields; and the warm damp bodies, still languid and soft, as if in a swoon, were bunched together by the men in gaiters and flung into the cart.

'There!' grunted Milly Masters, the housekeeper, throwing down her glasses. She was stitching too in the small dark room that overlooked the stable-yard. The jersey, the rough woollen jersey for her son, the boy who cleaned the church, was finished. 'The end o' that!' she muttered. Then she heard the cart. Wheels ground on the cobbles. Up she got. With her hands to her hair, her chestnut-coloured hair, she stood in the yard, in the wind.

'Coming!' she laughed, and the scar on her cheek lengthened. She unbolted the door of the game-room as Wing, the keeper, drove the cart over the cobbles. The birds were dead now, their claws gripped tight, though they gripped nothing. The leathery eyelids were creased greyly over their eyes. Mrs Masters the housekeeper, Wing the gamekeeper, took bunches of dead birds by the neck and flung them down on the slate floor of the game-larder. The slate floor became smeared and spotted with blood. The pheasants looked smaller now, as if their bodies had shrunk together. Then Wing lifted the tail of the cart and drove in the pins which secured it. The sides of the cart were stuck about with little grey-blue feathers and the floor was smeared and stained with blood. But it was empty.

'The last of the lot!' Milly Masters grinned as the cart drove off.

'Luncheon is served, ma'am,' said the butler. He pointed at the table; he directed the footman. The dish with the silver cover was placed precisely there where he pointed.

Miss Antonia laid her white film upon the basket; put away her silk; her thimble; stuck her needle through a piece of flannel; and hung her glasses on a hook upon her breast. Then she rose.

'Luncheon!' she barked in old Miss Rashleigh's ear. One second later old Miss Rashleigh stretched her leg out; gripped her stick; and rose too. Both old women advanced slowly to the table; and were tucked in by the butler and the footman, one at this end, one at that. Off came the silver cover. And there was the pheasant, featherless, gleaming; the thighs tightly pressed to its side; and little mounds of breadcrumbs were heaped at either end.

Miss Antonia drew the carving knife across the pheasant's breast firmly. She cut two slices and laid them on a plate. Deftly the footman whipped it from her, and old Miss Rashleigh raised her knife. Shots rang out in the wood under the window.

'Coming?' said old Miss Rashleigh, suspending her fork.

The branches flung and flaunted on the trees in the Park.

She took a mouthful of pheasant. Falling leaves flicked the window-pane; one or two stuck to the glass.

'In the Home Wood now,' said Miss Antonia. 'Hugh's last shoot.' She drew her knife down the other side of the breast. She added potatoes and gravy, Brussels sprouts and bread sauce methodically in a circle round the slices on her plate. The butler and the footman stood watching, like servers at a feast. The old ladies ate quietly; silently; nor did they hurry themselves; methodically they cleaned the bird. Bones only were left on their plates. Then the butler drew the decanter towards Miss Antonia, and paused for a moment with his head bent.

'Give it here, Griffiths,' said Miss Antonia, and took the carcass in her fingers and tossed it to the spaniel beneath the table.

'Coming closer,' said Miss Rashleigh, listening. The wind was rising. A brown shudder shook the air; leaves flew too fast to stick. The glass rattled in the windows.

'Birds wild,' Miss Antonia nodded, watching the helter-skelter.

Old Miss Rashleigh filled her glass. As they sipped their eyes became lustrous like half-precious stones held to the light. Slate blue were Miss Rashleigh's; Miss Antonia's red, like port. And their laces and their flounces seemed to quiver, as if their bodies were warm and languid underneath their feathers as they drank.

'It was a day like this, d'you remember?' said old Miss Rashleigh, fingering her glass. 'They brought him home . . . a bullet through his heart. A bramble, so they said. Tripped. Caught his foot . . . ' She chuckled as she sipped her wine.

'And John . . . ' said Miss Antonia. 'The mare, they said, put her foot in a hole. Died in the field. The hunt rode over him. He came home, too, on a shutter . . . ' They sipped again.

'Remember Lily?' said old Miss Rashleigh. 'A bad 'un.' She shook her head. 'Riding with a scarlet tassel on her cane . . . '

'Rotten at the heart!' cried Miss Antonia. 'Remember the Colonel's letter? "Your son rode as if he had twenty devils in him—charged at the head of his men!" Then one white devil—ah hah!' she sipped again.

'The men of our house,' began Miss Rashleigh. She raised her glass. She held it high, as if she toasted the mermaid carved in plaster on the fireplace. She paused. The guns were barking. Something cracked in the woodwork. Or was it a rat running behind the plaster?

'Always women . . . ' Miss Antonia nodded. 'The men of our house. Pink and white Lucy at the Mill—d'you remember?'

'Ellen's daughter at the Goat and Sickle,' Miss Rashleigh added.

'And the girl at the tailor's,' Miss Antonia murmured, 'where Hugh bought his riding breeches, the little dark shop on the right . . . '

'. . . that used to be flooded every winter. It's *his* boy,' Miss Antonia chuckled, leaning towards her sister, 'that cleans the church.'

There was a crash. A slate had fallen down the chimney. The great log had snapped in two. Flakes of plaster fell from the shield above the fireplace.

'Falling,' old Miss Rashleigh chuckled. 'Falling.'

'And who,' said Miss Antonia, looking at the flakes on the carpet, 'who's to pay?'

Crowing like old babies, indifferent, reckless, they laughed, crossed to the fireplace, and sipped their sherry by the wood ashes and the plaster, until each glass held only one drop of wine, reddish purple, at the bottom. And this the old women did not wish to part with, so it seemed; for they fingered their glasses, as they sat side by side by the ashes; but they never raised them to their lips.

'Milly Masters in the still-room,' began old Miss Rashleigh. 'She's our brother's . . . '

A shot barked beneath the window. It cut the string that held the rain. Down it poured, down, down, down, in straight rods, whipping the windows. Light faded from the carpet. Light faded in their eyes too, as they sat by the white ashes listening. Their eyes became like pebbles, taken from water; grey stones dulled and dried. And their hands gripped their hands like the claws of dead birds gripping nothing. And they shrivelled as if the bodies inside the clothes had shrunk. Then Miss Antonia raised her glass to the mermaid. It was the last toast; the last drop; she drank it off. 'Coming!' she croaked, and slapped the glass down. A door banged below. Then another. Then another. Feet could be heard trampling, yet shuffling, along the corridor towards the gallery.

'Closer! Closer!' grinned Miss Rashleigh, baring her three yellow teeth.

The immensely high door burst open. In rushed three great hounds and stood panting. Then there entered, slouching, the Squire himself in shabby gaiters. The dogs pressed round him, tossing their heads, snuffling at his pockets. Then they bounded forward. They smelt the meat. The floor of the gallery waved like a wind-lashed forest with the tails and backs of the great questing hounds. They snuffed the table. They pawed the cloth. Then with a wild neighing whimper they flung themselves upon the yellow spaniel who was gnawing the carcass under the table.

'Curse you, curse you!' howled the Squire. But his voice was weak, as if he shouted against a wind. 'Curse you, curse you!' he shouted, now cursing his sisters.

Miss Antonia and Miss Rashleigh rose to their feet. The great dogs had seized the spaniel. They worried him, they mauled him with their great yellow teeth. The Squire swung a leather knotted tawse this way, that way, cursing the dogs, cursing his sisters, in the voice that sounded so loud yet was so weak. With one lash he curled to the ground the vase of chrysanthemums. Another caught old Miss Rashleigh on the cheek. The old woman staggered backwards. She fell against the mantelpiece. Her stick, striking wildly, struck the shield above the fireplace. She fell with a thud upon the ashes. The shield of the Rashleighs crashed from the wall. Under the mermaid, under the spears, she lay buried.

The wind lashed the panes of the glass; shots volleyed in the

Park and a tree fell. And then King Edward in the silver frame
slid, toppled and fell too.

The grey mist had thickened in the carriage. It hung down like a
veil; it seemed to put the four travellers in the corners at a great
distance from each other, though in fact they were as close as a
third-class railway carriage could bring them. The effect was
strange. The handsome if elderly, the well-dressed, if rather
shabby woman who had got into the train at some station in the
Midlands seemed to have lost her shape. Her body had become all
mist. Only her eyes gleamed, changed, lived all by themselves, it
seemed; eyes without a body; blue-grey eyes seeing something
invisible. In the misty air they shone out, they moved, so that
in the sepulchral atmosphere—the windows were blurred, the
lamps haloed with fog—they were like lights dancing, will-o'-the-
wisps that move, people say, over the graves of unquiet sleepers in
churchyards. An absurd idea? Mere fancy! Yet, after all, since
there is nothing that does not leave some residue, and memory is
a light that dances in the mind when the reality is buried, why
should not the eyes there, gleaming, moving, be the ghost of a
family, of an age, of a civilization dancing over the grave?
    The train slowed down. One after another, lamps stood up;
held their yellow heads erect for a second; then were felled. Up
they stood again as the train slid into the station. The lights
massed and blazed. And the eyes in the corner? They were shut;
the lids were closed. They saw nothing. Perhaps the light was too
strong. And, of course, in the full blaze of the station lamps it was
plain—she was quite an ordinary, rather elderly woman travelling
to London on some quite ordinary piece of business—something
connected with a cat or a horse or a dog. She reached for her
suitcase, rose, and took the pheasants from the rack. But did she,
all the same, as she opened the carriage door and stepped out,
murmur 'Chk, Chk,' as she passed?

THE DUCHESS AND THE JEWELLER

OLIVER BACON lived at the top of a house overlooking the Green Park.* He had a flat; chairs jutted out at the right angles—chairs covered in hide. Sofas filled the bays of the windows—sofas covered in tapestry. The windows, the three long windows, had the proper allowance of discreet net and figured satin. The mahogany sideboard bulged discreetly with the right brandies, whiskeys and liqueurs. And from the middle window he looked down upon the glossy roofs of fashionable cars packed in the narrow straits of Piccadilly. A more central position could not be imagined. And at eight in the morning he would have his break-fast brought in on a tray by a manservant; the manservant would unfold his crimson dressing-gown; he would rip his letters open with his long pointed nails and would extract thick white cards of invitation upon which the engraving stood up roughly from duchesses, countesses, viscountesses and Honourable Ladies. Then he would wash; then he would eat his toast; then he would read his paper by the bright burning fire of electric coals.

'Behold Oliver,' he would say, addressing himself. 'You who began life in a filthy little alley, you who . . . ' and he would look down at his legs, so shapely in their perfect trousers; at his boots; at his spats. They were all shaped, shining; cut from the best cloth by the best scissors in Savile Row.* But he dismantled him-self often and became again a little boy in a dark alley. He had once thought that the height of his ambition—selling stolen dogs to fashionable women in Whitechapel. And once he had been done.* 'Oh, Oliver,' his mother had wailed. 'Oh, Oliver! When will you have sense, my son?' . . . Then he had gone behind a counter; had sold cheap watches; then he had taken a wallet to Amsterdam . . . At that memory he would chuckle—the old Oliver remem-bering the young. Yes, he had done well with the three diamonds; also there was the commission on the emerald. After that he went into the private room behind the shop in Hatton Garden* the room with the scales, the safe, the thick magnifying glasses. And then ... and then ... He chuckled. When he passed through the knots of jewellers in the hot evening who were discussing prices, gold mines, diamonds, reports from South Africa, one of them would lay a finger to the side of his nose and murmur, 'Hum-m-m,' as he passed. It was no more than a murmur; no more than a nudge on the shoulder, a finger on the nose, a buzz that ran through the cluster of jewellers in Hatton Garden on a hot afternoon—oh, many years ago now! But still Oliver felt it purring down his spine, the nudge, the murmur that meant, 'Look at him—young Oliver, the young jeweller—there he goes.' Young he was then. And he dressed better and better; and had, first a hansom cab; then a car; and first he went up to the dress circle, then down into the stalls. And he had a villa at Richmond,* overlooking the river, with trellises of red roses; and Mademoiselle used to pick one every morning and stick it in his buttonhole.

'So,' said Oliver Bacon, rising and stretching his legs. 'So ...'

And he stood beneath the picture of an old lady on the mantelpiece and raised his hands. 'I have kept my word,' he said, laying his hands together, palm to palm, as if he were doing homage to her. 'I have won my bet.' That was so; he was the richest jeweller in England; but his nose, which was long and flexible, like an elephant's trunk, seemed to say by its curious quiver at the nostrils (but it seemed as if the whole nose quivered, not only the nostrils) that he was not satisfied yet; still smelt something under the ground a little further off. Imagine a giant hog in a pasture rich with truffles; after unearthing this truffle and that, still it smells a bigger, a blacker truffle under the ground further off. So Oliver snuffed always in the rich earth of Mayfair* another truffle, a blacker, a bigger further off.

Now then he straightened the pearl in his tie, cased himself in his smart blue overcoat; took his yellow gloves and his cane; and swayed as he descended the stairs and half snuffed, half sighed through his long sharp nose as he passed out into Piccadilly. For was he not still a sad man, a dissatisfied man, a man who seeks something that is hidden, though he had won his bet?

He swayed slightly as he walked, as the camel at the zoo sways from side to side when it walks along the asphalt paths laden with grocers and their wives eating from paper bags and throwing little bits of silver paper crumpled up on to the path. The camel despises the grocers; the camel is dissatisfied with its lot; the camel sees the blue lake and the fringe of palm trees in front of it. So the great jeweller, the greatest jeweller in the whole world, swung down Piccadilly, perfectly dressed, with his gloves, with his cane; but dissatisfied still, till he reached the dark little shop, that was famous in France, in Germany, in Austria, in Italy, and all over America—the dark little shop in the street off Bond Street.*

As usual he strode through the shop without speaking, though the four men, the two old men, Marshall and Spencer, and the two young men, Hammond and Wicks, stood straight behind the counter as he passed and looked at him, envying him. It was only with one finger of the amber-coloured glove, waggling, that he acknowledged their presence. And he went in and shut the door of his private room behind him.

Then he unlocked the grating that barred the window. The cries of Bond Street came in; the purr of the distant traffic. The light from reflectors at the back of the shop struck upwards. One tree waved six green leaves, for it was June. But Mademoiselle had married Mr Pedder of the local brewery—no one stuck roses in his buttonhole now.

'So,' he half sighed, half snorted, 'so . . .'

Then he touched a spring in the wall and slowly the panelling slid open, and behind it were the steel safes, five, no, six of them, all of burnished steel. He twisted a key; unlocked one; then another. Each was lined with a pad of deep crimson velvet; in each lay jewels—bracelets, necklaces, rings, tiaras, ducal coronets; loose stones in glass shells; rubies, emeralds, pearls, diamonds. All safe, shining, cool, yet burning, eternally, with their own compressed light.

'Tears!' said Oliver, looking at the pearls.

'Heart's blood!' he said, looking at the rubies.

'Gunpowder!' he continued, rattling the diamonds so that they flashed and blazed.

'Gunpowder enough to blow up Mayfair—sky high, high,

high!' He threw his head back and made a sound like a horse neighing as he said it.

The telephone buzzed obsequiously in a low muted voice on his table. He shut the safe.

'In ten minutes,' he said. 'Not before.' And he sat down at his desk and looked at the heads of the Roman emperors that were graved on his sleeve links. And again he dismantled himself and became once more the little boy playing marbles in the alley where they sell stolen dogs on Sunday. He became that wily astute little boy, with lips like wet cherries. He dabbled his fingers in ropes of tripe; he dipped them in pans of frying fish; he dodged in and out among the crowds. He was slim, lissome, with eyes like licked stones. And now—now—the hands of the clock ticked on. One, two, three, four—The Duchess of Lambourne waited his pleasure; the Duchess of Lambourne, daughter of a hundred Earls. She would wait for ten minutes on a chair at the counter. She would wait his pleasure. She would wait till he was ready to see her. He watched the clock in its shagreen case. The hand moved on. With each tick the clock handed him—so it seemed— pâté de foie gras; a glass of champagne; another of fine brandy; a cigar costing one guinea. The clock laid them on the table beside him, as the ten minutes passed. Then he heard soft slow footsteps approaching; a rustle in the corridor. The door opened. Mr Hammond flattened himself against the wall.

'Her Grace!' he announced.

And he waited there, flattened against the wall.

And Oliver, rising, could hear the rustle of the dress of the Duchess as she came down the passage. Then she loomed up, filling the door, filling the room with the aroma, the prestige, the arrogance, the pomp, the pride of all the Dukes and Duchesses swollen in one wave. And as a wave breaks, she broke, as she sat down, spreading and splashing and falling over Oliver Bacon the great jeweller, covering him with sparkling bright colours, green, rose, violet; and odours; and iridescences; and rays shooting from fingers, nodding from plumes, flashing from silk; for she was very large, very fat, tightly girt in pink taffeta, and past her prime. As a parasol with many flounces, as a peacock with many feathers, shuts its flounces, folds it feathers, so she subsided and shut herself as she sank down in the leather armchair.

'Good morning, Mr Bacon,' said the Duchess. And she held out her hand which came through the slit of her white glove. And Oliver bent low as he shook it. And as their hands touched the link was forged between them once more. They were friends, yet enemies; he was master, she was mistress; each cheated the other, each needed the other, each feared the other, each felt this and knew this every time they touched hands thus in the little back room with the white light outside, and the tree with its six leaves, and the sound of the street in the distance and behind them the safes.

'And today, Duchess—what can I do for you today?' said Oliver, very softly.

The Duchess opened; her heart, her private heart, gaped wide. And with a sigh, but no words, she took from her bag a long wash-leather pouch—it looked like a lean yellow ferret. And from a slit in the ferret's belly she dropped pearls—ten pearls. They rolled from the slit in the ferret's belly—one, two, three, four— like the eggs of some heavenly bird.

'All that's left me, dear Mr Bacon,' she moaned. Five, six, seven—down they rolled, down the slopes of the vast mountain sides that fell between her knees into one narrow valley—the eighth, the ninth, and the tenth. There they lay in the glow of the peach-blossom taffeta. Ten pearls.

'From the Appleby cincture,' she mourned. 'The last . . . the last of them all.'

Oliver stretched out and took one of the pearls between finger and thumb. It was round, it was lustrous. But real was it, or false? Was she lying again? Did she dare?

She laid her plump padded finger across her lips. 'If the Duke knew . . . ' she whispered. 'Dear Mr Bacon, a bit of bad luck . . . '

Been gambling again, had she?

'That villain! That sharper!' she hissed.

The man with the chipped cheek bone? A bad 'un. And the Duke was straight as a poker; with side whiskers; would cut her off, shut her up down there if he knew—what I know, thought Oliver, and glanced at the safe.

'Araminta, Daphne, Diana,' she moaned. 'It's for *them*.'

The Ladies Araminta, Daphne, Diana—her daughters. He knew them; adored them. But it was Diana he loved.

'You have all my secrets,' she leered. Tears slid; tears fell; tears, like diamonds, collecting powder in the ruts of her cherry-blossom cheeks.

'Old friend,' she murmured, 'old friend.'

'Old friend,' he repeated, 'old friend,' as if he licked the words.

'How much?' he queried.

She covered the pearls with her hand.

'Twenty thousand,' she whispered.

But was it real or false, the one he held in his hand? The Appleby cincture—hadn't she sold it already? He would ring for Spencer or Hammond. 'Take it and test it,' he would say. He stretched to the bell.

'You will come down tomorrow?' she urged, she interrupted. 'The Prime Minister—His Royal Highness . . . ' She stopped. 'And Diana,' she added.

Oliver took his hand off the bell.

He looked past her, at the backs of the houses in Bond Street. But he saw, not the houses in Bond Street, but a dimpling river; and trout rising and salmon; and the Prime Minister; and himself too; in white waistcoats; and then, Diana. He looked down at the pearl in his hand. But how could he test it, in the light of the river, in the light of the eyes of Diana? But the eyes of the Duchess were on him.

'Twenty thousand,' she moaned. 'My honour!'

The honour of the mother of Diana! He drew his cheque book towards him; he took out his pen.

'Twenty,' he wrote. Then he stopped writing. The eyes of the old woman in the picture were on him—of the old woman, his mother.

'Oliver!' she warned him. 'Have sense? Don't be a fool!'

'Oliver!' the Duchess entreated—it was 'Oliver' now, not 'Mr Bacon'. 'You'll come for a long weekend?'

Alone in the woods with Diana! Riding alone in the woods with Diana!

'Thousand,' he wrote, and signed it.

'Here you are,' he said.

And there opened all the flounces of the parasol, all the plumes of the peacock, the radiance of the wave, the swords and spears of Agincourt,* as she rose from her chair. And the two old men and the two young men, Spencer and Marshall, Wicks and Hammond, flattened themselves behind the counter envying him as he led her through the shop to the door. And he waggled his yellow glove in their faces, and she held her honour—a cheque for twenty thousand pounds with his signature—quite firmly in her hands.

'Are they false or are they real?' asked Oliver, shutting his private door. There they were, ten pearls on the blotting paper on the table. He took them to the window. He held them under his lens to the light . . . This, then, was the truffle he had routed out of the earth! Rotten at the centre—rotten at the core!

'Forgive me, oh my mother!' he sighed, raising his hands as if he asked pardon of the old woman in the picture. And again he was a little boy in the alley where they sold dogs on Sunday.

'For,' he murmured, laying the palms of his hands together, 'it is to be a long weekend.'

LAPPIN AND LAPINOVA

THEY were married. The wedding march pealed out. The pigeons fluttered. Small boys in Eton jackets threw rice; a fox-terrier sauntered across the path; and Ernest Thorburn led his bride to the car through that small inquisitive crowd of complete strangers which always collects in London to enjoy other people's happiness or unhappiness. Certainly he looked handsome and she looked shy. More rice was thrown, and the car moved off.

That was on Tuesday. Now it was Saturday. Rosalind had still to get used to the fact that she was Mrs Ernest Thorburn. Perhaps she never would get used to the fact that she was Mrs Ernest Anybody, she thought, as she sat in the bow window of the hotel looking over the lake to the mountains, and waited for her husband to come down to breakfast. Ernest was a difficult name to get used to. It was not the name she would have chosen. She would have preferred Timothy, Antony, or Peter. He did not look like Ernest either. The name suggested the Albert Memorial, mahogany sideboards, steel engravings of the Prince Consort with his family—her mother-in-law's dining-room in Porchester Terrace* in short.

But here he was. Thank goodness he did not look like Ernest—no. But what did he look like? She glanced at him sideways. Well, when he was eating toast he looked like a rabbit. Not that anyone else would have seen a likeness to a creature so diminutive and timid in this spruce, muscular young man with the straight nose, the blue eyes, and the very firm mouth. But that made it all the more amusing. His nose twitched very slightly when he ate. So did her pet rabbit's. She kept watching his nose twitch; and then she had to explain, when he caught her looking at him, why she laughed.

'It's because you're like a rabbit, Ernest,' she said. 'Like a wild rabbit,' she added, looking at him. 'A hunting rabbit; a King Rabbit; a rabbit that makes laws for all the other rabbits.'

Ernest had no objection to being that kind of rabbit, and since it amused her to see him twitch his nose—he had never known that his nose twitched—he twitched it on purpose. And she laughed and laughed; and he laughed too, so that the maiden ladies and the fishing man and the Swiss waiter in his greasy black jacket all guessed right; they were very happy. But how long does such happiness last? they asked themselves; and each answered according to his own circumstances.

At lunch time, seated on a clump of heather beside the lake, 'Lettuce, rabbit?' said Rosalind, holding out the lettuce that had been provided to eat with the hard-boiled eggs. 'Come and take it out of my hand,' she added, and he stretched out and nibbled the lettuce and twitched his nose.

'Good rabbit, nice rabbit,' she said, patting him, as she used to pat her tame rabbit at home. But that was absurd. He was not a tame rabbit, whatever he was. She turned it into French. 'Lapin,' she called him. But whatever he was, he was not a French rabbit. He was simply and solely English—born in Porchester Terrace, educated at Rugby,* now a clerk in His Majesty's Civil Service. So she tried 'Bunny' next; but that was worse. 'Bunny' was someone plump and soft and comic;* he was thin and hard and serious. Still, his nose twitched. 'Lappin,' she exclaimed suddenly; and gave a little cry as if she had found the very word she looked for.

'Lappin, Lappin, King Lappin,' she repeated. It seemed to suit him exactly; he was not Ernest, he was King Lappin. Why? She did not know.

When there was nothing new to talk about on their long solitary walks—and it rained, as everyone had warned them that it would rain; or when they were sitting over the fire in the evening, for it was cold, and the maiden ladies had gone and the fishing man, and the waiter only came if you rang the bell for him, she let her fancy play with the story of the Lappin tribe. Under her hands—she was sewing, he was reading—they became very real, very vivid, very amusing. Ernest put down the paper and helped her. There were the black rabbits and the red; there were the enemy rabbits and the friendly. There were the wood in which they lived and the outlying prairies and the swamp. Above all there was King Lappin, who, far from having only the one trick—that he twitched his nose—became, as the days passed, an animal of the greatest character. Rosalind was always finding new qualities in him. But above all he was a great hunter.

'And what,' said Rosalind, on the last day of the honeymoon, 'did the King do today?'

In fact they had been climbing all day; and she had worn a blister on her heel; but she did not mean that.

'Today,' said Ernest twitching his nose as he bit the end off his cigar, 'he chased a hare.' He paused; struck a match, and twitched again.

'A woman hare,' he added.

'A white hare!' Rosalind exclaimed, as if she had been expecting this. 'Rather a small hare; silver grey; with big bright eyes?'

'Yes,' said Ernest, looking at her as she had looked at him, 'a smallish animal; with eyes popping out of her head, and two little front paws dangling.' It was exactly how she sat, with her sewing dangling in her hands; and her eyes, that were so big and bright, were certainly a little prominent.

'Ah, Lapinova,' Rosalind murmured.

'Is that what she's called,' said Ernest, 'the real Rosalind?' He looked at her. He felt very much in love with her.

'Yes; that's what she's called,' said Rosalind: 'Lapinova.' And before they went to bed that night it was all settled. He was King Lappin; she was Queen Lapinova. They were the very opposite of each other; he was bold and determined; she wary and undependable. He ruled over the busy world of rabbits; her world was a desolate, mysterious place, which she ranged mostly by moonlight. All the same, their territories touched; they were King and Queen of the land of rabbits and hares.

Thus when they came back from their honeymoon they possessed a private world, inhabited, save for the one white hare, entirely by rabbits. No one guessed that there was such a place, and that of course made it all the more amusing. It made them feel, more even than most young married couples, in league together against the rest of the world. Often they looked slyly at each other when people talked about rabbits and woods and traps and shooting. Or they winked furtively across the table when

Aunt Mary said that she could never bear to see a hare in a dish— it looked so like a baby; or when John, Ernest's sporting brother, told them what price rabbits were fetching that autumn in Wiltshire, skins and all. Sometimes when they wanted a gamekeeper, or a poacher or a Lord of the Manor, they amused themselves by distributing the parts among their friends. Ernest's mother, Mrs Reginald Thorburn, for example, fitted the part of the Squire to perfection. But it was all secret—that was the point of it; nobody save themselves knew that such a world existed.

Without that world, how, Rosalind wondered, could she ever have endured the golden-wedding party when all the Thorburns assembled at Porchester Terrace to celebrate the fiftieth anniversary of that union which had been so blessed—had it not produced Ernest Thorburn?—and so fruitful—had it not produced nine other sons and daughters into the bargain, many themselves married and also fruitful? She dreaded that party. But it was inevitable. As she walked upstairs she felt bitterly that she was an only child and an orphan at that; a mere drop among all those Thorburns assembled in the great drawing-room with the shiny satin wallpaper and the lustrous family portraits. The living Thorburns much resembled the painted; save that instead of painted lips they had real lips; out of which came jokes; jokes about schoolrooms, and how they had pulled the chair from under the governess; jokes about frogs and how they had put them between the virgin sheets of maiden ladies. As for herself, she had never even made an apple-pie bed. Holding her present in her hand, she advanced towards her mother-in-law, sumptuous in yellow satin; and towards her father-in-law, decorated with a rich yellow carnation. All round them on tables and chairs there were golden tributes, some nestling in cotton wool; others branching resplendent—candlesticks; cigar boxes; chains; each stamped with the goldsmith's proof that it was solid gold, hallmarked, authentic. But her present was only a little pinchbeck box pierced with holes; an old sand caster, an eighteenth-century relic, once used to sprinkle sand over wet ink. Rather a senseless present, she felt, in an age of blotting-paper; and as she proffered it, she saw in front of her the stubby black handwriting in which her mother-in-law, when they were engaged, had expressed the hope that 'My son will make you happy.' No, she was not happy. Not at all happy. She looked at Ernest, straight as a ramrod with a nose like all the noses in the family portraits, a nose that never twitched at all.

Then they went down to dinner. She was half hidden by the great chrysanthemums that curled their red and gold petals into large tight balls. Everything was gold. A gold-edged card with gold initials intertwined recited the list of all the dishes that would be set one after another before them. She dipped her spoon in a plate of clear golden soup. The raw white fog outside had been turned by the lamps into a golden mesh that blurred the edges of the plates and gave the pineapples a rough golden skin. Only she herself in her white wedding dress peering ahead of her with her prominent eyes seemed insoluble as an icicle.

As the dinner wore on, however, the room grew steamy with heat. Beads of perspiration stood out on the men's foreheads. She felt that her icicle was being turned to water. She was being melted; dispersed; dissolved into nothingness; and would soon faint. Then through the surge in her head and the din in her ears she heard a woman's voice exclaim, 'But of course they breed so!'

The Thorburns—yes; they breed so, she echoed; looking at all the round red faces that seemed doubled in the giddiness that overcame her; and magnified in the gold mist that enhaloed them. 'They breed so.' Then John bawled:

'Little devils! Shoot 'em! Jump on 'em with big boots! That's the only way to deal with 'em . . . rabbits!'

At that word, that magic word, she revived. Peeping between the chrysanthemums she saw Ernest's nose twitch. It rippled, it ran, with successive twitches. And at that a mysterious catastrophe befell the Thorburns. The golden table became a moor with the gorse in full bloom; the din of voices turned to one peal of lark's laughter ringing down from the sky. It was a blue sky— clouds passed slowly. And they had all been changed—the Thorburns. She looked at her father-in-law, a furtive little man with dyed moustaches. His foible was collecting things—seals, enamel boxes, trifles from eighteenth-century dressing-tables which he hid from his wife in the drawers of his desk. Now she saw him as he was—a poacher, stealing off with his coat bulging with pheasants and partridges to drop them stealthily into a three-legged pot in his smoky little cottage. That was her real father-in-law—a poacher. And Celia, the unmarried daughter, who always nosed out other people's secrets, the little things they wished to hide— she was a white ferret with pink eyes, and a nose clotted with earth from her horrid underground nosings and pokings. Slung round men's shoulders, in a net, and thrust down a hole—it was a pitiable life, Celia's; it was none of her fault. So she saw Celia. And then she looked at her mother-in-law—whom they dubbed The Squire. Flushed, coarse, a bully—she was all that, as she stood returning thanks, but now that Rosalind—that is Lapinova—saw her, she saw behind her the decayed family mansion, the plaster peeling off the walls, and heard her, with a sob in her voice, giving thanks to her children (who hated her) for a world that had ceased to exist. There was a sudden silence. They all stood with their glasses raised; they all drank; then it was over.

'Oh, King Lappin!' she cried as they went home together in the fog. 'If your nose hadn't twitched just at that moment, I should have been trapped!'

'But you're safe,' said King Lappin, pressing her paw.

'Quite safe,' she answered, pressing his too.

And they drove back through the Park, King and Queen of the marsh, of the mist, of the gorse-scented moor.

Thus time passed; one year; two years of time. And on a winter's night, which happened by a coincidence to be the anniversary of the golden-wedding party—but Mrs Reginald Thorburn was dead; the house was to let; and there was only a caretaker in residence—Ernest came home from the office. They had a nice little home; half a house above a saddler's shop in South Kensington, not far from the tube station. It was cold, with fog in the air, and Rosalind was sitting over the fire sewing.

'What d'you think happened to me today?' she began as soon as he had settled himself down with his legs stretched to the blaze. 'I was crossing the stream when—'

'What stream?' Ernest interrupted her.

'The stream at the bottom, where our wood meets the black wood,' she explained.

Ernest looked completely blank for a moment.

'What the deuce are you talking about?' he asked.

'My dear Ernest!' she cried in dismay. 'King Lappin,' she added, dangling her little front paws in the firelight. But his nose did not twitch. Her hands—they turned to hands—clutched the stuff she was holding; her eyes popped half out of her head. It took him five minutes at least to change from Ernest Thorburn to King Lappin; and while she waited she felt a load on the back of her neck, as if somebody were about to wring it. At last he changed to King Lappin; his nose twitched; and they spent the evening roaming the woods much as usual.

But she slept badly. In the middle of the night she woke, feeling as if something strange had happened to her. She was stiff and cold. At last she turned on the light and looked at Ernest lying beside her. He was sound asleep. He snored. But even though he snored, his nose remained perfectly still. It looked as if it had never twitched at all. Was it possible that he was really Ernest; and that she was really married to Ernest? A vision of her mother-in-law's dining-room came before her; and there they sat, she and Ernest, grown old, under the engravings, in front of the sideboard . . . It was their golden-wedding day. She could not bear it.

'Lappin, King Lappin!' she whispered, and for a moment his nose seemed to twitch of its own accord. But he still slept. 'Wake up, Lappin, wake up!' she cried.

Ernest woke; and, seeing her sitting bolt upright beside him, he asked:

'What's the matter?'

'I thought my rabbit was dead!' she whimpered. Ernest was angry.

'Don't talk such rubbish, Rosalind,' he said. 'Lie down and go to sleep.'

He turned over. In another moment he was sound asleep and snoring.

But she could not sleep. She lay curled up on her side of the bed, like a hare in its form. She had turned out the light, but the street-lamp lit the ceiling faintly, and the trees outside made a lacy network over it as if there were a shadowy grove on the ceiling in which she wandered, turning, twisting, in and out, round and round, hunting, being hunted, hearing the bay of hounds, and horns blowing . . . until the maid drew the blinds and brought their early tea.

Next day she could settle to nothing. She seemed to have lost something. She felt as if her body had shrunk; it had grown small, and black and hard. Her joints seemed stiff too, and when she looked in the glass, which she did several times as she wandered about the flat, her eyes seemed to burst out of her head, like currants in a bun. The rooms also seemed to have shrunk. Large pieces of furniture jutted out at odd angles and she found herself knocking against them. At last she put on her hat and went out. She walked along the Cromwell Road; and every room she passed and peered into seemed to be a dining-room where people sat eating under steel engravings, with thick yellow lace curtains, and mahogany sideboards. At last she reached the Natural History Museum,* she used to like it when she was a child. But the first thing she saw when she went in was a stuffed hare standing on sham snow with pink glass eyes. Somehow it made her shiver all over. Perhaps it would be better when dusk fell. She went home and sat over the fire, without a light, and tried to imagine that she was out alone on a moor: and there was a stream rushing; and beyond the stream a dark wood. But she could get no farther than the stream. At last she squatted down on the bank on the wet grass, and sat crouched in her chair, with her hands dangling empty, and her eyes glazed, like glass eyes, in the firelight. Then there was the crack of a gun . . . She started as if she had been shot. It was only Ernest turning his key in the door. She waited, trembling. He came in and switched on the light. There he stood tall, handsome, rubbing his hands that were red with cold.

'Sitting in the dark?' he said.

'Oh, Ernest, Ernest!' she cried starting up in her chair.

'Well, what's up now?' he asked briskly, warming his hands at the fire.

'It's Lapinova . . . ' she faltered, glancing wildly at him out of her great startled eyes. 'She's gone, Ernest. I've lost her!'

Ernest frowned. He pressed his lips tight together. 'Oh, that's what's up, is it?' he said, smiling rather grimly at his wife. For ten seconds he stood there, silent; and she waited, feeling hands tightening at the back of her neck.

'Yes,' he said at length. 'Poor Lapinova . . . ' He straightened his tie at the looking-glass over the mantelpiece.

'Caught in a trap,' he said, 'killed,' and sat down and read the newspaper.

So that was the end of that marriage.

THE LEGACY

'For Sissy Miller.' Gilbert Clandon, taking up the pearl brooch that lay among a litter of rings and brooches on a little table in his wife's drawing-room, read the inscription: 'For Sissy Miller, with my love.'

It was like Angela to have remembered even Sissy Miller, her secretary. Yet how strange it was, Gilbert Clandon thought once more, that she had left everything in such order—a little gift of some sort for every one of her friends. It was as if she had foreseen her death. Yet she had been in perfect health when she left the house that morning, six weeks ago; when she stepped off the kerb in Piccadilly* and the car had killed her.

He was waiting for Sissy Miller. He had asked her to come; he owed her, he felt, after all the years she had been with them, this token of consideration. Yes, he went on, as he sat there waiting, it was strange that Angela had left everything in such order. Every friend had been left some little token of her affection. Every ring, every necklace, every little Chinese box—she had a passion for little boxes—had a name on it. And each had some memory for him. This he had given her; this—the enamel dolphin with the ruby eyes—she had pounced upon one day in a back street in Venice. He could remember her little cry of delight. To him, of course, she had left nothing in particular, unless it were her diary. Fifteen little volumes, bound in green leather, stood behind him on her writing table. Ever since they were married, she had kept a diary. Some of their very few—he could not call them quarrels, say tiffs—had been about that diary. When he came in and found her writing, she always shut it or put her hand over it. 'No, no, no,' he could hear her say, 'After I'm dead—perhaps.' So she had left it him, as her legacy. It was the only thing they had not shared when she was alive. But he had always taken it for granted that she would outlive him. If only she had stopped one moment, and had thought what she was doing, she would be alive now. But she had stepped straight off the kerb, the driver of the car had said at the inquest. She had given him no chance to pull up. . . . Here the sound of voices in the hall interrupted him.

'Miss Miller, Sir,' said the maid.

She came in. He had never seen her alone in his life, nor, of course, in tears. She was terribly distressed, and no wonder. Angela had been much more to her than an employer. She had been a friend. To himself, he thought, as he pushed a chair for her and asked her to sit down, she was scarcely distinguishable from any other woman of her kind. There were thousands of Sissy Millers—drab little women in black carrying attaché cases. But Angela, with her genius for sympathy, had discovered all sorts of qualities in Sissy Miller. She was the soul of discretion, so silent; so trustworthy, one could tell her anything, and so on.

Miss Miller could not speak at first. She sat there dabbing her eyes with her pocket handkerchief. Then she made an effort.

'Pardon me, Mr Clandon,' she said.

He murmured. Of course he understood. It was only natural. He could guess what his wife had meant to her.

'I've been so happy here,' she said, looking round. Her eyes rested on the writing table behind him. It was here they had worked—she and Angela. For Angela had her share of the duties that fall to the lot of the wife of a prominent politician. She had been the greatest help to him in his career. He had often seen her and Sissy sitting at that table—Sissy at the typewriter, taking down letters from her dictation. No doubt Miss Miller was thinking of that, too. Now all he had to do was to give her the brooch his wife had left her. A rather incongruous gift it seemed. It might have been better to have left her a sum of money, or even the typewriter. But there it was—'For Sissy Miller, with my love.' And, taking the brooch, he gave it her with the little speech that he had prepared. He knew, he said, that she would value it. His wife had often worn it. . . . And she replied, as she took it, almost as if she too had prepared a speech, that it would always be a treasured possession. . . . She had, he supposed, other clothes upon which a pearl brooch would not look quite so incongruous. She was wearing the little black coat and skirt that seemed the uniform of her profession. Then he remembered—she was in mourning, of course. She too had had her tragedy—a brother, to whom she was devoted, had died only a week or two before Angela. In some accident was it? He could not remember—only Angela telling him; Angela, with her genius for sympathy, had been terribly upset. Meanwhile, Sissy Miller had risen. She was putting on her gloves. Evidently she felt that she ought not to intrude. But he could not let her go without saying something about her future. What were her plans? Was there any way in which he could help her?

She was gazing at the table, where she had sat at her typewriter, where the diary lay. And, lost in her memories of Angela, she did not at once answer his suggestion that he should help her. She seemed for a moment not to understand. So he repeated:

'What are your plans, Miss Miller?'

'My plans? Oh, that's all right, Mr Clandon,' she exclaimed. 'Please don't bother yourself about me.'

He took her to mean that she was in no need of financial assistance. It would be better, he realised, to make any suggestion of that kind in a letter. All he could do now was to say as he pressed her hand. 'Remember, Miss Miller, if there's any way in which I can help you, it will be a pleasure. . . . ' Then he opened the door. For a moment, on the threshold, as if a sudden thought had struck her, she stopped.

'Mr Clandon,' she said, looking straight at him for the first time, and for the first time he was struck by the expression, sympathetic yet searching, in her eyes. 'If at any time,' she continued, 'there's anything I can do to help you, remember, I shall feel it, for your wife's sake, a pleasure . . . '

With that she was gone. Her words and the look that went with them were unexpected. It was almost as if she believed, or hoped, that he would have need of her. A curious, perhaps a fantastic idea occurred to him as he returned to his chair. Could it be, that during all those years when he had scarcely noticed her, she, as the novelists say, had entertained a passion for him? He caught his own reflection in the glass as he passed. He was over fifty; but he could not help admitting that he was still, as the looking-glass showed him, a very distinguished-looking man.

'Poor Sissy Miller!' he said, half laughing. How he would have liked to share that joke with his wife! He turned instinctively to her diary. 'Gilbert,' he read, opening it at random, 'looked so wonderful. . . . ' It was as if she had answered his question. Of course, she seemed to say, you're very attractive to women. Of course Sissy Miller felt that too. He read on. 'How proud I am to be his wife!' And he had always been very proud to be her husband. How often when they dined out somewhere he had looked at her across the table and said to himself, she is the loveliest woman here! He read on. That first year he had been standing for Parliament. They had toured his constituency. 'When Gilbert sat down the applause was terrific. The whole audience rose and sang: "For he's a jolly good fellow." I was quite overcome.' He remembered that, too. She had been sitting on the platform beside him. He could still see the glance she cast at him, and how she had tears in her eyes. And then? He turned the pages. They had gone to Venice. He recalled that happy holiday after the election. 'We had ices at Florians.' He smiled—she was still such a child, she loved ices. 'Gilbert gave me a most interesting account of the history of Venice. He told me that the Doges* . . . ' she had written it all out in her schoolgirl hand. One of the delights of travelling with Angela had been that she was so eager to learn. She was so terribly ignorant, she used to say, as if that were not one of her charms. And then—he opened the next volume—they had come back to London. 'I was so anxious to make a good impression. I wore my wedding dress.' He could see her now sitting next old Sir Edward; and making a conquest of that formidable old man, his chief. He read on rapidly, filling in scene after scene from her scrappy fragments. 'Dined at the House of Commons. . . . To an evening party at the Lovegroves. Did I realise my responsibility, Lady L. asked me, as Gilbert's wife?' Then as the years passed—he took another volume from the writing table—he had become more and more absorbed in his work. And she, of course, was more often alone. It had been a great grief to her, apparently, that they had had no children. 'How I wish,' one entry read, 'that Gilbert had a son!' Oddly enough he had never much regretted that himself. Life had been so full, so rich as it was. That year he had been given a minor post in the government. A minor post only, but her comment was: 'I am quite certain now that he will be Prime Minister!' Well, if things had gone differently, it might have been so. He paused here to speculate upon what might have been. Politics was a gamble, he reflected; but the game wasn't over yet. Not at fifty. He cast his eyes rapidly over more pages, full of the little trifles, the insignificant, happy, daily trifles that had made up her life.

He took up another volume and opened it at random. 'What a coward I am! I let the chance slip again. But it seemed selfish to bother him about my own affairs, when he has so much to think about. And we so seldom have an evening alone.' What was the meaning of that? Oh here was the explanation—it referred to her work in the East End.* 'I plucked up courage and talked to Gilbert at last. He was so kind, so good. He made no objection.' He remembered that conversation. She had told him that she felt so idle, so useless. She wished to have some work of her own. She wanted to do something—she had blushed so prettily, he remembered, as she said it sitting in that very chair—to help others. He had bantered her a little. Hadn't she enough to do looking after him, after her home? Still if it amused her of course he had no objection. What was it? Some district? Some committee? Only she must promise not to make herself ill. So it seemed that every Wednesday she went to Whitechapel.* He remembered how he hated the clothes she wore on those occasions. But she had taken it very seriously it seemed. The diary was full of references like this: 'Saw Mrs Jones. . . . She has ten children. . . . Husband lost his arm in an accident. . . . Did my best to find a job for Lily.' He skipped on. His own name occurred less frequently. His interest slackened. Some of the entries conveyed nothing to him. For example: 'Had a heated argument about socialism with B. M.' Who was B. M.? He could not fill in the initials; some woman, he supposed, that she had met on one of her committees. 'B. M. made a violent attack upon the upper classes. . . . I walked back after the meeting with B. M. and tried to convince him. But he is so narrow-minded.' So B. M. was a man—no doubt one of those 'intellectuals' as they call themselves, who are so violent, as

Angela said, and so narrow-minded. She had invited him to come and see her apparently. 'B. M. came to dinner. He shook hands with Minnie!' That note of exclamation gave another twist to his mental picture. B. M. it seemed wasn't used to parlourmaids; he had shaken hands with Minnie. Presumably he was one of those tame working men who air their views in ladies' drawing-rooms. Gilbert knew the type, and had no liking for this particular specimen, whoever B. M. might be. Here he was again. 'Went with B. M. to the Tower of London. . . . He said revolution is bound to come. . . . He said we live in a Fool's Paradise.' That was just the kind of thing B. M. would say—Gilbert could hear him. He could also see him quite distinctly—a stubby little man, with a rough beard, red tie, dressed as they always did in tweeds, who had never done an honest day's work in his life. Surely Angela had the sense to see through him? He read on. 'B. M. said some very disagreeable things about . . . ' The name was carefully scratched out. 'I told him I would not listen to any more abuse of . . . ' Again the name was obliterated. Could it have been his own name? Was that why Angela covered the page so quickly when he came in? The thought added to his growing dislike of B. M. He had had the impertinence to discuss him in this very room. Why had Angela never told him? It was very unlike her to conceal anything; she had been the soul of candour. He turned the pages, picking out every reference to B. M. 'B. M. told me the story of his childhood. His mother went out charring. . . . When I think of it, I can hardly bear to go on living in such luxury. . . . Three guineas for one hat!' If only she had discussed the matter with him, instead of puzzling her poor little head about questions that were much too difficult for her to understand! He had lent her books. Karl Marx. 'The Coming Revolution.'* The initials B. M., B. M., B. M., recurred repeatedly. But why never the full name? There was an informality, an intimacy in the use of initials that was very unlike Angela. Had she called him B. M. to his face? He read on. 'B. M. came unexpectedly after dinner. Luckily, I was alone.' That was only a year ago. 'Luckily'—why luckily?—'I was alone.' Where had he been that night? He checked the date in his engagement book. It had been the night of the Mansion

House* dinner. And B. M. and Angela had spent the evening alone! He tried to recall that evening. Was she waiting up for him when he came back? Had the room looked just as usual? Were there glasses on the table? Were the chairs drawn close together? He could remember nothing—nothing whatever, nothing except his own speech at the Mansion House dinner. It became more and more inexplicable to him—the whole situation: his wife receiving an unknown man alone. Perhaps the next volume would explain. Hastily he reached for the last of the diaries—the one she had left unfinished when she died. There on the very first page was that cursed fellow again. 'Dined alone with B. M. . . . He became very agitated. He said it was time we understood each other. . . . I tried to make him listen. But he would not. He threatened that if I did not . . . ' the rest of the page was scored over. She had written 'Egypt. Egypt. Egypt.' * over the whole page. He could not make out a single word; but there could be only one interpretation: the scoundrel had asked her to become his mistress. Alone in his room! The blood rushed to Gilbert Clandon's face. He turned the pages rapidly. What had been her answer? Initials had ceased. It was simply 'he' now. 'He came again. I told him I could not come to any decision. . . . I implored him to leave me.' He had forced himself upon her in this very house? But why hadn't she told him? How could she have hesitated for an instant? Then: 'I wrote him a letter.' Then pages were left blank. Then there was this: 'No answer to my letter.' Then more blank pages; and then this. 'He has done what he threatened.' After that—what came after that? He turned page after page. All were blank. But there, on the very day before her death, was this entry: 'Have I the courage to do it too?' That was the end.

Gilbert Clandon let the book slide to the floor. He could see her in front of him. She was standing on the kerb in Piccadilly. Her eyes stared; her fists were clenched. Here came the car. . . .

He could not bear it. He must know the truth. He strode to the telephone.

'Miss Miller!' There was silence. Then he heard someone moving in the room.

'Sissy Miller speaking'—her voice at last answered him.

'Who,' he thundered, 'is B. M.?'

He could hear the cheap clock ticking on her mantelpiece; then a long drawn sigh. Then at last she said:

'He was my brother.'

He *was* her brother; her brother who had killed himself.

'Is there,' he heard Sissy Miller asking, 'anything that I can explain?'

'Nothing!' he cried. 'Nothing!'

He had received his legacy. She had told him the truth. She had stepped off the kerb to rejoin her lover. She had stepped off the kerb to escape from him.

EXPLANATORY NOTES

The Mark on the Wall

4 *the asphodel meadows*: an asphodel is a flowering plant of the lily family ('daffodil' is a corruption of asphodel) associated with death in Greek legend. The Plain of Asphodel is where the dead dwell in the Underworld in Homer's *The Odyssey*.

5 *Troy three times over*: an ancient fortress city situated near the Dardanelles in Asia Minor, Troy was captured and sacked by the Greeks who tricked the Trojans with their wooden horse stratagem around 1184 BC. By the time Woolf wrote this story, excavations at Troy had revealed no fewer than nine superimposed cities.

Kingsway . . . Charles the First: Kingsway, a thoroughfare in central London opened in 1905 by Edward VII (reigned 1901–10) and named in his honour, was conceived in response to Victorian traffic congestion. It runs north–south between the Aldwych and Holborn. Charles I reigned from 1625 to 1649, when he was beheaded.

Tall flowers with purple tassels to them perhaps: almost certainly columbines.

7 *Whitaker's Table of Precedency . . . Landseer prints*: in every edition of Whitaker's *Almanack* (published annually since 1868) there is a 'Table of Precedency [or Precedence] in the United Kingdom' which sets out a social hierarchy from the 'Sovereign' down to 'Naval, Military, Air, and Other Esquires by Office'. Sir Edwin Landseer (1802–73) became celebrated for his sentimental paintings of animals. Many of his most popular images enjoyed mass circulation in the form of prints.

the South Downs: the treeless chalk uplands forming a ridge across the southern English counties of Sussex and Hampshire.

Kew Gardens

11 *a hundred stalks . . . slightly clubbed at the end*: probably gladioli.

12 *suddenly a kiss . . . kisses all my life*: Eleanor's response to this kiss anticipates Clarissa Dalloway's ecstatic reaction to being kissed by Sally Seton in *Mrs Dalloway*: see David Bradshaw (ed.), Virginia Woolf, *Mrs Dalloway*, Oxford World's Classics (Oxford: OUP, 2000), 30.

13 *Thessaly*: in antiquity, a fertile area of north-eastern Greece noted for its cavalry and magicians. Its chief cities were Larissa, Crannon, and Pherae.

16 *a Chinese pagoda*: situated within the Royal Botanic Gardens at Kew, south-west London, is the Great Pagoda. Built in 1761–2, it is 163 ft. high.

An Unwritten Novel

18 *the map of the line framed opposite*: the story takes place on a train journey from London (beginning, almost certainly, at Victoria Station) to East-bourne, Sussex, and there is a framed map of the line above the narrator's seat. Three Bridges and Lewes, mentioned a little further on in the story, are stops on a line which Woolf knew well from travelling between her homes in London and Sussex.

'Peace between Germany . . . it's all in The Times!': the Versailles Peace Treaty between Germany and the allies brought a formal end to the First World War. Signed on 28 June 1919 in the Palace of Versailles, near Paris, and ratified on Saturday, 10 January 1920 at the French Ministry of Foreign Affairs, it succeeded in establishing both the League of Nations and a German sense of grievance which helped sow the seeds of the Second World War. The Radical economist and politician Francesco Saverio Nitti became Prime Minister of Italy in June 1919 and was present at both the signing and ratification of the Treaty. However, his administration proved both unstable and unpopular and Nitti was replaced as Prime Minister in mid-1920. The 'Sandhills murder' refers to the murder of Kathleen Elsie Breaks of Bradford at St Anne's-on-Sea, Lancashire, on 24 December 1919, first reported in *The Times* in an item headed 'Seaside Murder Charge: Woman's Body Found Among Sandhills' on 27 December 1919, 7, and widely covered in the early part of 1920 when her murderer was brought to trial. But the crash of a passenger train at Doncaster, 'the habits of birds, Leonardo da Vinci . . . [and] high wages and the cost of living' are not 'all in *The Times*' for Sunday, 11 January 1920 (the day in question if 'Peace . . . was *yesterday* officially ushered in at Paris', as *The Times* is said to report) as the newspaper was not (and is not) published on a Sunday. Nor do these items of news appear together in another issue of *The Times* from around this date, suggesting that Woolf simply invented them.

21 *More like President Kruger than Prince Albert*: the Afrikaner statesman S. J. Paul(us) Kruger (1825–1904), a robust and hirsute man, was head of the Provisional Government during the first Boer War (1880–1) and President of the South African Republic (1883–1902). During the second Boer (or South African) War (1899–1902) he spent a great deal of time in Europe, vainly seeking alliances against Britain. Albert (1819–61), tall, slim, and intellectual, was Prince Consort of Queen Victoria, whom he married in 1840.

22 *Croydon*: then a small town in West Sussex, now a large residential borough of south Greater London.

24 *the Andes . . . gold and silver*: the narrator imagines Sir Francis Drake (*c*.1543–96) and his men ambushing a party of Spanish mule-drivers and their cargo of gold and silver on the Isthmus of Panama at the northern end of the Andes range of mountains. The Andes system extends for about 7,250 km. from Cape Horn to the Isthmus of Panama up the

western side of South America, separating a narrow coastal belt from the rest of the continent.

25 *travels in—shall we say buttons?*: that is, he is an itinerant salesman of buttons.

He reads 'Truth': a weekly newspaper published between 1877 and 1957.

26 *St Paul's*: designed by Sir Christopher Wren (1632–1723), begun in 1675 and completed in 1710, the present St Paul's Cathedral is the fourth to occupy its site at the top of Ludgate Hill, central London.

28 *merry thought*: 'the forked bone between the neck and breast of a bird, the wishbone' (*OED*).

A Haunted House

31 *the Downs*: see note to p. 7 on the South Downs.

Monday or Tuesday

32 *Flaunted . . . torn, sunk, assembled*: the glide, dive, switch, and swoop of this sentence has a distinctly Gerard Manley Hopkins-like feel. On 23 July 1919, Woolf wrote to her friend Janet Case: 'Have you read the poems of a man, who is dead, called Gerard Hopkins? I like them better than any poetry for ever so long; partly because they're so difficult, but also because instead of writing mere rhythms and sense as most poets do, he makes a very strange jumble; so that what is apparently pure nonsense is at the same time very beautiful, and not nonsense at all' (*The Letters of Virginia Woolf*, ed. Nigel Nicolson and Joanne Trautman (6 vols.; London: Hogarth Press, 1975–80), ii, 379). Hopkins (1844–89) published hardly anything during his lifetime and his collected *Poems* did not appear until 1918, initially to some puzzlement and then to great acclaim.

Blue and Green

33 *lustre*: 'Any of a decorative group of prismatic glass pendants attached to a chandelier or other ornament; a cut-glass chandelier or candelabrum' (*OED*). Musing on the impending decoration of the drawing-rooms at Monks House (the home she and Leonard Woolf shared at Rodmell in Sussex), Woolf wrote to her sister Vanessa on 13 June 1926: 'Would I be allowed some rather garish but vibrating and radiating green and red lustres on the mantlepiece? Showers of glass, shaped like long fingers in a bunch—you know my taste that way' (*Letters*, iii. 273).

The String Quartet

35 *landaus with bays*: four-wheeled enclosed carriages pulled by dark reddish-brown horses.

Regent Street is up, and the Treaty signed . . . influenza: Regent Street is one of the principal shopping streets of London. The central, curved portion of the street between Piccadilly Circus and Oxford Street is known as the Quadrant. For 'the Treaty', see note to p. 18. The influenza pandemic of 1918–19 killed 228,917 Britons and well over 20 million people worldwide.

35 *The King*: in 1920 the King of the United Kingdom of Great Britain and Northern Ireland and the Emperor of India was George V (reigned 1910–36).

36 *Malmesbury*: a small town in Wiltshire.

A Society

40 *the London Library*: founded in 1841 and situated at 14 St James's Square since 1845. Woolf's father, Sir Leslie Stephen (1832–1904), was the fifth President of the Library.

41 *'From a Window'* . . . *something of that kind*: these titles and names suggest that it is *From a College Window* (1906) by the novelist and critic A. C. Benson (1862–1925).

42 *the objects of life were to produce good people and good books*: these tenets are clearly indebted to the ideas expounded in *Principia Ethica* (1903) by the Cambridge philosopher G. E. Moore (1873–1958). Moore believed that goodness is the fundamental ethical concept which cannot be defined or analysed in terms of anything simpler. His ideas had an enormous influence on the Bloomsbury Group.

Ethiopian Prince . . . *taps upon the behind*: during the course of the 'Dreadnought Hoax' (10 February 1910), Woolf, her brother Adrian, the painter Duncan Grant, and two other men, posing as the Emperor of Abyssinia and his suite, paid a bogus official visit of inspection to HMS *Dreadnought*, then moored at Weymouth on the Dorset coast. Subsequently, Grant was punished by the Flag Commander of the ship with two taps on the bottom.

43 *killed at Trafalgar*: Nelson defeated the French at the Battle of Trafalgar in 1805, thus bringing a halt to Napoleon's European ambitions.

the Law Courts: opened in 1882, the Law Courts (or Royal Courts of Justice) are located on the Strand in central London.

the Royal Academy: founded in 1768 and devoted to the fine arts, the Royal Academy of Arts is located at Burlington House, Piccadilly. Piccadilly, extending from Piccadilly Circus to Hyde Park Corner, is one of the two ancient highways leading westward out of central London (the other being Oxford Street).

'O for the touch . . . *the way to glory—'*: this cluster of (more or less accurate) quotations comprises the following: 'But O for the touch of a vanished hand, | And the sound of a voice that is still!', from 'Break, Break, Break' by Alfred Lord Tennyson (1809–92); 'Home is the sailor, home from the sea, | And the hunter home from the hill', from *Underwoods* (1887) (XXI, 'Requiem') by Robert Louis Stevenson (1850–94); 'He gave his bridle reins a shake', from 'It was a' for our rightfu' king', a song by Robert Burns (1759–96); 'Love is sweet, love is brief' has not

been located, but Woolf may have misremembered 'Love is sweet, and so are flowers', the first line of 'Love Ephemeral' by Christina Rossetti (1830–94); 'Spring, the sweet spring, is the year's pleasant king', from *Summers Last Will and Testament*, a comedy by Thomas Nashe (1567–1601); 'Oh, to be in England | Now that April's there', are the opening lines of 'Home-Thoughts from Abroad' by Robert Browning (1812–89); 'Men must work and women must weep' is a slight variation on a line from 'The Three Fishers' by Charles Kingsley (1819–75); 'The path of duty was the way to glory', from Tennyson's 'Ode on the Death of the Duke of Wellington' (1852), line 202. The point of all this is that there was a perception that the only paintings acceptable to the Royal Academy were those on an uplifting, sentimental, moralistic, or patriotic theme, often derived from a literary source.

44 *'Daughters of England!'*: borrowed from *The Daughters of England: Their Position in Society, Character and Responsibilities* (1842) by Sarah Ellis, née Strickney (1810?–72).

Castalia: not the most appropriate name, as Castalia herself is quick to acknowledge when she becomes pregnant, in that it derives from the Latin word for 'chaste'.

Dulwich: Dulwich Village is an affluent and attractive district of suburban south-east London.

Once in a hundred years the Aloe flowered: in a story called 'Prelude', but originally entitled 'The Aloe', by 'Katherine Mansfield' (the pseudonym of the New Zealand writer Kathleen Mansfield Beauchamp, 1888–1923), a mother tells her daughter, Kezia, that the American aloe flowers once every hundred years; another name for the aloe is the century plant. Mansfield's *Prelude* (1918) was the second book published by Leonard and Virginia Woolf at their Hogarth Press.

Sappho: a late-seventh-century BC Greek lyric poet born on the island of Lesbos (from which the word 'lesbian' derives). In her surviving work, Sappho's subject matter is almost exclusively that of female friends and family and she seems to have written primarily for her group of female admirers on the island.

46 *Cassandra*: in Greek myth, the prophetic daughter of Priam, King of Troy (see note to p. 5), and his wife Hecuba. It was Cassandra's fate to always prophesy truthfully but never to be believed.

48 *Judith . . . to bear children*: Judith, the heroine of the biblical Book of Judith (regarded by Jews and Protestants as apocryphal), 'is a beautiful and wealthy widow who, in defense of God and country, first captivates and then decapitates Holofernes, the Assyrian general besieging her hometown, Bethulia of Samaria' (Bruce M. Metzger and Michael D. Coogan, *The Oxford Companion to the Bible* (New York and Oxford: Oxford University Press, 1993), 400). The Book of Judith is extremely ironic and this mood is reflected both in 'A Society' as a whole and in

particular in this tilt at contemporary eugenicist preoccupations with sound breeding and social hygiene.

49 *Is Kensington . . . a baronet or only a knight?*: an affluent area of central London in the vicinity of Hyde Park, Kensington was then (and still is) 'a nice place to live in'. A baronet is a 'member of the lowest hereditary titled British order, with the status of commoner but able to use the prefix "Sir"' (*OED*), whereas one meaning of the word 'knight' is 'A man awarded a title (now non-hereditary) by a sovereign in recognition of personal merit or services rendered, ranking below a baronet, and entitled to be styled *Sir*' (*OED*).

50 *Mr Wells . . . Mr Walpole*: H. G. Wells (1866–1946) was a well-known novelist and polemicist whose intellectual energy Woolf admired but whose literary skills she largely deplored. Arnold Bennett (1867–1931) is the novelist and reviewer whose work Woolf attacks in her key essay 'Character in Fiction' (1924; repr. in *The Essays of Virginia Woolf*, ed. Andrew NcNeillie (6 vols.; London: Hogarth Press, 1986–), iii. 420–38) and elsewhere. It was Bennett's *Our Women* (1920) which prompted Woolf to write 'A Society': see Introduction, pp. xvii–xix. The best-known novel of Compton Mackenzie (1883–1972) is probably *Whisky Galore* (1947), but by 1920 he had already received praise for *Sinister Street* (1913–14), *Sylvia Scarlett* (1918), and *Sylvia and Michael* (1919). Stephen McKenna (1888–1956) was the popular author of *Sonia* (1917) and *Sonia Married* (1919), while Hugh Walpole (1884–1941), a New Zealander, sold even more books and became a close friend of Woolf's in the 1930s.

51 *'War! War! War! Declaration of War!'*: Britain declared war on Germany on 4 August 1914.

'In 1760 . . . In 1900 on the other hand —': 1760 marked the mid-point of the Seven Years War (1756–63) between Britain and Prussia on one side and France, Austria, Russia, Sweden, and Saxony on the other. Notable battles included those at Minden (1759), Quebec (1759), and Plassey (1757), with less significant engagements taking place at Liegnitz and Torgau in 1760. The year 1797 saw the fall of the Venetian Republic during the first phase of the Revolutionary and Napoleonic Wars. On 2 December 1804 Napoleon proclaimed himself Emperor of the French, leading to British treaties with Russia, Austria, and Sweden in the War of the Third Coalition. The Battle of Königgrätz-Sadowa (3 July 1866) marked the decisive Prussian victory in the 1866 war against Austria. The Franco–Prussian War lasted from 1870 to 1871 and ended in crushing defeats for the French at the Battles of Sedan and Metz, before the German Second Reich was declared in Versailles' hall of mirrors. The Boxer Rising of 1900 was finally crushed in Beijing on 14 August.

52 *Mr Lloyd George*: David Lloyd George (1863–1945), 1st Earl Lloyd George, was Prime Minister from 1916 to 1922. He laid the foundations

of what would become the welfare state and was acclaimed as 'The Man Who Won the War'. But by 1920 he was a more controversial figure, with the Liberals blaming him for the decline of their party after 1918, the Conservatives opposing his radicalism, and the Labour Party objecting to his handling of industrial issues.

53 *a weekend at Lahore*: Lahore is now the second largest city in Pakistan. It first came under British rule in 1849.

the Treaty of Peace had just been signed: that is, the Peace of Versailles: see note to p. 18 above.

Solid Objects

54 *'Politics be damned!'*: the German theologian and politician Christoph Blumhardt (1842–1919) once said, 'I am proud to stand before you as a man; and if politics cannot tolerate a human being, then let politics be damned.'

57 *the Temple*: there are four Inns of Court—the Inner Temple, the Middle Temple, Gray's Inn, and Lincoln's Inn—and the Temple is the general name for the Inner and Middle Temples. Ownership of the Temple site, which lies north of the Victoria Embankment on the boundary between Westminster and the City of London, was granted to these two Inns of Court by James I in 1609.

58 *Barnes Common*: covers about 120 acres in the south-west of London.

In the Orchard

60 *'Ce pays . . . le mieux . . . '*: 'Truly, this country is one of the corners of the world where young girls burst into laughter most readily' (French). This quotation is taken from *Ramuntcho* (1897), a novel by Pierre Loti (1850–1923), Part I, 112. 'Pierre Loti' was the pseudonym of Julien Viaud.

Hymns Ancient and Modern: the standard hymn book of the Church of England. Edited by the Revd Sir H. W. Baker (1821–77), it first appeared in 1861.

61 *the golden feather of the church tower*: that is, its weather-vane.

The Shooting Party

69 *the coloured photograph of York Minster*: Milly Masters is travelling south on the London and North Eastern Railway line, which ran from Scotland to King's Cross Station in London via York. Begun in 1154, York Minster is the cathedral and seat of the Archbishop of York. As the story begins in 'the Midlands', Milly has probably got on the train at either Sheffield or Chesterfield.

'Chk,' 'Chk': Milly Masters, Miss Antonia, and Miss Rashleigh all mimic the sound of a pheasant during the course of the story.

70 *the coat of arms . . . the mermaid; and the spears*: in the late sixteenth and early seventeenth centuries, the term 'mermaid' was often used for a

prostitute. As a heraldic symbol, the mermaid is depicted with long flowing golden hair and with a comb in her left hand and a mirror in her right. The 'spear side' is the male line of descent in a family.

70 *an egg-shaped baldish head . . . with a flourish beneath*: it has been signed by Edward (1841–1910), eldest son of Queen Victoria, who reigned as Edward VII (1901–10).

71 *old Miss Rashleigh*: styled thus, she must be Miss Antonia's elder sister.

The Duchess and the Jeweller

77 *a house overlooking the Green Park*: Bacon's flat is on the north side of Piccadilly (see note to p. 43). Green Park covers 53 acres between Piccadilly and Constitution Hill in central London and was made into a Royal Park by Charles II (reigned 1660–85).

Savile Row: situated just round the corner from Bacon's flat, Savile Row is world-famous for its gentlemen's tailors, such as Gieves and Hawkes at No. 1 and Strickland and Sons at No. 15.

selling stolen dogs . . . had been done: Woolf describes dog-stealing in the East End's Whitechapel (see note to p. 97) district in chapter 4 of *Flush: A Biography* (1933). To be 'done' is a slang term meaning to be prosecuted and serve time.

taken a wallet to Amsterdam . . . Hatton Garden: that is, smuggled diamonds and/or other jewels to the Dutch city famous for its trade in precious gems. Hatton Garden has been the street at the centre of the London diamond trade since the early nineteenth century.

78 *a villa at Richmond*: Leonard and Virginia Woolf lived at Richmond between 1915 and 1924, but in the redbrick Hogarth House (built in 1748) rather than a redbrick house of more recent construction, as is almost certainly implied here. The word 'villa' had been sneeringly associated with suburban sprawl since the mid-nineteenth century.

Mayfair: the wealthy and prestigious area of central London bounded to the south by Piccadilly, to the north by Oxford Street, to the east by Regent Street, and to the west by Park Lane.

79 *Bond Street*: a premier shopping street extending from Piccadilly to Oxford Street through Mayfair.

83 *the swords and spears of Agincourt*: at the Battle of Agincourt (1415) the French were defeated by Henry V of England (reigned 1413–22). Although 'swords and spears' certainly figured in the battle, it was Henry's 5,000 archers who proved decisive.

Lappin and Lapinova

84 *the Albert Memorial . . . Porchester Terrace*: the Albert Memorial was erected in Hyde Park, London, between 1862 and 1872 as the national monument to Albert, Prince Consort (the second son of Ernest, Duke of Saxe-Coburg, and Louise, daughter of Duke Augustus of Saxe-

Coburg-Altenburg), who had died in 1861 (see note to p. 21). It stands 175 ft. high. Porchester Terrace is in Bayswater, just north of Hyde Park.

85 *Rugby*: founded in 1567, Rugby School came to great prominence in the nineteenth century under the headmastership of Thomas Arnold (1795–1842), who was renowned for his promotion of 'muscular Christianity'.

   'Bunny'. . . . someone plump and soft and comic: this could well be a friendly dig at David 'Bunny' Garnett (1892–1981), novelist, critic, and member of the Bloomsbury Group. In 1922 he published *Lady into Fox*, a fantastic tale about a young woman who becomes a vixen.

91 *Cromwell Road . . . Natural History Museum*: the Natural History Museum on the Cromwell Road, South Kensington, London, was designed in the Romanesque style by Alfred Waterhouse (1830–1905) and first opened to the public in 1881.

The Legacy

93 *Piccadilly*: see note to p. 43.

96 *the Doges*: the chief magistrate of Venice from about AD 697 to the fall of the Venetian Republic in 1797 was known as the Doge.

97 *her work in the East End*: by choosing the name Angela for her character and giving her a commitment to philanthropic work in the East End of London, Woolf evokes memories of Angela Georgina Burdett-Coutts, Baroness Burdett-Coutts (1814–1906), possibly the most energetic British philanthropist of the nineteenth century.

   Whitechapel: a district of the East End, adjacent to the City of London, synonymous in the Victorian and Edwardian periods with the miseries of poverty, overcrowding, pollution, and deprivation.

98 *Karl Marx. 'The Coming Revolution.'*: Karl (Heinrich) Marx (1818–83), German revolutionary and founder of modern communism, was the son of a Jewish lawyer. In his *Communist Manifesto* (1848) Marx attacked the state as the instrument of oppression, religion and culture as ideologies of the capitalist class, and predicted the overthrow of the capitalist system. He settled in London in 1849, studied economics, and wrote, among other books, the first volume of his greatest (and unfinished) work, *Das Kapital* (1867). *The Coming Revolution in England* (1884) is a 32-page pamphlet by Henry Mayers Hyndman (1842–1921), in his day as famous a Socialist as William Morris, George Bernard Shaw, and Keir Hardie.

99 *Mansion House*: the Mansion House is the official residence of the Lord Mayor of London for his year in office. Begun in 1739 to the design of George Dance, it was largely completed by 1752, though years of remodelling were to follow.

   'Egypt. Egypt. Egypt.': presumably an allusion to the bondage of the Israelites in Egypt, as described in the second book of the Old Testament (Exodus 1–14). Angela feels trapped between her wifely fidelity to her husband and her love for Sissy Miller's brother.

D. H. LAWRENCE

The Rainbow
Sons and Lovers
The White Peacock
The Widowing of Mrs Holroyd and Other Plays
Women in Love

KATHERINE MANSFIELD

Selected Stories

MARIE STOPES

Married Love

ROBERT TRESSELL

The Ragged Trousered Philanthropists

VIRGINIA WOOLF

Between the Acts
Flush
Jacob's Room
Mrs Dalloway
The Mark on the Wall and Other Short Fiction
Night and Day
Orlando: A Biography
A Room of One's Own and Three Guineas
To the Lighthouse
The Voyage Out
The Waves
The Years

W. B. YEATS

The Major Works

CHARLES DICKENS	**A Tale of Two Cities**
GEORGE DU MAURIER	**Trilby**
MARIA EDGEWORTH	**Castle Rackrent**
GEORGE ELIOT	**Daniel Deronda** **The Lifted Veil and Brother Jacob** **Middlemarch** **The Mill on the Floss** **Silas Marner**
SUSAN FERRIER	**Marriage**
ELIZABETH GASKELL	**Cranford** **The Life of Charlotte Brontë** **Mary Barton** **North and South** **Wives and Daughters**
GEORGE GISSING	**New Grub Street** **The Odd Women**
EDMUND GOSSE	**Father and Son**
THOMAS HARDY	**Far from the Madding Crowd** **Jude the Obscure** **The Mayor of Casterbridge** **The Return of the Native** **Tess of the d'Urbervilles** **The Woodlanders**
WILLIAM HAZLITT	**Selected Writings**
JAMES HOGG	**The Private Memoirs and Confessions of a Justified Sinner**
JOHN KEATS	**The Major Works** **Selected Letters**
CHARLES MATURIN	**Melmoth the Wanderer**
JOHN RUSKIN	**Selected Writings**
WALTER SCOTT	**The Antiquary** **Ivanhoe**

WALTER SCOTT	**Rob Roy**
MARY SHELLEY	**Frankenstein** **The Last Man**
ROBERT LOUIS STEVENSON	**Strange Case of Dr Jekyll and** **Mr Hyde and Other Tales** **Treasure Island**
BRAM STOKER	**Dracula**
JOHN SUTHERLAND	**So You Think You Know Jane Austen?** **So You Think You Know Thomas Hardy?**
WILLIAM MAKEPEACE THACKERAY	**Vanity Fair**
OSCAR WILDE	**The Importance of Being Earnest and** **Other Plays** **The Major Works** **The Picture of Dorian Gray**
ELLEN WOOD	**East Lynne**
DOROTHY WORDSWORTH	**The Grasmere and Alfoxden Journals**
WILLIAM WORDSWORTH	**The Major Works**

The Oxford World's Classics Website

www.oup.com/uk/worldsclassics

- Information about new titles
- Explore the full range of Oxford World's Classics
- Links to other literary sites and the main OUP webpage
- Imaginative competitions, with bookish prizes
- Articles by editors
- Extracts from Introductions
- Special information for teachers and lecturers

www.oup.com/uk/worldsclassics

American Literature

Authors in Context

British and Irish Literature

Children's Literature

Classics and Ancient Literature

Colonial Literature

Eastern Literature

European Literature

History

Medieval Literature

Oxford English Drama

Poetry

Philosophy

Politics

Religion

The Oxford Shakespeare

A complete list of Oxford World's Classics, including Authors in Context, Oxford English Drama, and the Oxford Shakespeare, is available in the UK from the Marketing Services Department, Oxford University Press, Great Clarendon Street, Oxford OX2 6DP, or visit the website at www.oup.com/uk/worldsclassics.

In the USA, visit www.oup.com/us/owc for a complete title list.

Oxford World's Classics are available from all good bookshops. In case of difficulty, customers in the UK should contact Oxford University Press Bookshop, 116 High Street, Oxford OX1 4BR.